GUIDE TO

MODERN ART

IN EUROPE

Published by the Junior Council of
THE MUSEUM OF MODERN ART,
New York
with the cooperation of Pan American World Airways

Edited by Dolores B. Lamanna

Distributed by Doubleday & Company, Inc.,
Garden City, New York

PHOTOGRAPH CREDITS: Hein Engelskirchen GDL, Krefeld, p. 47 bottom; Foto Friebel, Sursee, p. 110 bottom; Vladimir Fyman, Prague, p. 14; Fritz Henle, New York, p. 69 top; Jesper Hom, Copenhagen, p. 15; Adalbert Komers-Lindenbach, Vienna, p. 6; Photo Chiffelle, Chexbres, p. 110 top; Monique Porée, Rouen, p. 29 top; Soichi Sunami, New York, pp. 83, 118; Filip Tas, Antwerp, p. 9; Bernward Wember, Krefeld, p. 47 top

PREFACE

The *Guide to Modern Art in Europe* is designed to help the traveler locate the numerous collections—large and small, important and less significant—of modern art in Europe. Many European museums in small towns off the standard tourist routes house breath-taking art collections which are well worth a detour.

It is not the aim of this directory to be more than descriptive; no explanations or comments are offered. Entries are limited to art works produced after 1850.

Included in this book are: 1. Museums of modern art. 2. General art museums which contain permanent collections of modern art. 3. Museums or other institutions which regularly schedule temporary exhibitions of modern art. 4. Private collections which are regularly open to the public.

Most art museums have changing loan exhibitions. Inquiries should be made locally to determine what, if any, special modern art exhibitions are currently being presented. It is also advisable to ascertain the local public holidays in each country as museums are often closed on these days. Regulations about taking photographs vary; when in doubt, don't.

Museums and collections are presented alphabetically within each city; cities are alphabetized within countries. Names of local art periodicals or other pertinent publications are given, where possible, following each country's entries. Users of this guide might also find of interest the international art magazines: *Art International,* published in Zurich, *L'Oeil* and *XXᵉ Siècle,* published in Paris, *Metro,* published in Milan and *Quadrum,* published in Brussels. *The New Architecture of Europe,* by G. E. Kidder Smith, published by Meridian Books and Penguin Books, describes 225 contemporary European buildings and contains a useful bibliography of other architectural publications.

No two persons would come to the same decision on every entry in a catalogue of this type. Many reasons dictated the inclusions; it is hoped museum-goers will find at least some of them rewarding. It is inconceivable that a guidebook could be published with enough speed to outdistance the frequent changes in hours, admission charges and other data. Every reasonable effort has been made to obtain the most up-to-date and accurate information; however, errors and omissions are inevitable—and regretted.

It would have been impossible to compile this book without the enthusiastic and invaluable cooperation which I received from the staffs of embassies, consulates and information offices of the countries represented and several United States Foreign Service posts. I am extremely grateful to these persons. I am also indebted to the many staff members and friends of the Museum of Modern Art who provided the benefit of their knowledge and personal travel experience. In particular I wish to thank Porter A. McCray, William S. Lieberman, Staff Adviser to the Junior Council and Gerald W. Whitted, Publications Editor, Pan American World Airways.

Many other persons have contributed their time and energy; especially, Dorothy Mayhall, Irene Hudtwalcker, John Carter and the staff of the Museum Library. Finally, my special thanks go to Lucy Lippard for her research assistance.

D.B.L.

INTRODUCTION

One hundred years ago a grand tour of Europe would schedule an impressive sequence of treasure houses and monuments devoted to the panorama of the past. Such a tour, however, ignored contemporary art. Today, no traveler interested in the arts will miss these splendors. He can, however, also experience the adventure of the art of his own time. The offerings are many and this guide lists some 400.

Every capital of Europe accessible by air has collections of modern art. These often include the art of the recent past. Many cities also offer exhibition galleries and parks devoted to contemporary painting and sculpture which are sometimes included within the frame of a larger institution.

Cities, however, hold no monopoly on modern art in Europe. Several provincial towns, a surprising number, house important private or specialized collections. Also, many small but choice galleries have opened since the last war, for instance a garland of museums devoted to aspects of modern art is strung along the Côte d'Azur. This guide includes information about these. It also suggests other possible visits, from a vintner's museum in Pauillac to a restaurant in Zurich. In all, 27 countries of Europe are represented.

Guidebooks, red and blue, have served as companions to several generations of travelers. This is the first devoted to modern art. It was initiated, quite properly, by a group of men and women in New York whose numerous activities augment the regular program of the Museum of Modern Art.

Although the guide is intended for the interested tourist, the art "professional" will find it as necessary as comfortable shoes.

WILLIAM S. LIEBERMAN
Curator, Drawings and Prints
The Museum of Modern Art, New York

Garden, Museum des 20. Jahrhunderts, Vienna

AUSTRIA

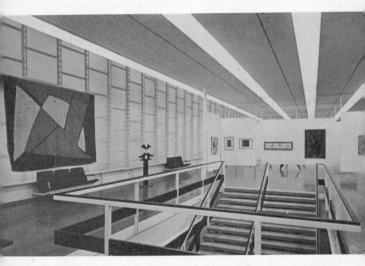

Museum des 20. Jahrhunderts, Vienna

Graz [*Steiermark*]

• NEUE GALERIE (of the Landesmuseum Joanneum), Sackgasse 16, Tel: 8 69 15. Painting, sculpture and prints of 19 and 20 centuries.

Hours: Monday, Tuesday and Friday, 9–12 and 3–5; other days, 9–12.

Admission: 2.50 schillings; students, 1.50 schillings.

Linz [Oberösterreich]

• NEUE GALERIE DER STADT LINZ, Hauptplatz 8, Tel: 2 68 51. Painting, prints, posters and other graphic arts of the 19 and 20 centuries including works by Klinger, Hofer, Liebermann, Busch.

Hours: Closed Monday; open Tuesday and Thursday, 10–9; other days, 10–6.

Admission: 2 schillings; students, 0.50 schilling.

Vienna [Wien]

• GRAPHISCHE SAMMLUNG ALBERTINA (Albertina Graphic Art Collection), Augustinerstrasse 1, Tel: 52 57 69. World's largest collection of drawings and prints, including works of the 19 and 20 centuries.

Hours: Exhibition hall: Wednesday, 10–6; Saturday, 10–12; Sunday and holidays, 10–1; other days, 10–4. Study room: closed Friday, Saturday and Sunday; open Monday, Tuesday and Thursday, 10–4; Wednesday, 2–4.

Admission: October 1–March 31, Sunday and holidays, free; other times: 5 schillings; students, free.

• HISTORISCHES MUSEUM DER STADT WIEN (Historical Museum of the City of Vienna), Karlsplatz, Tel: 45 16 61. Includes a collection of 19 and 20 century Austrian painting with works by Klimt, Gerstl, Kokoschka, Kolig, Schiele, Böckl and others.

Hours: Closed Monday; open Saturday and Sunday, 9:15–1; other days, 9:15–6.

Admission: 5 schillings.

• MUSEUM DES 20. JAHRHUNDERTS (Museum of the 20 Century), Schweizergarten, Tel: 65 51 21. Painting, sculpture and prints from 1900 to the present including works by Rodin, Schiele, Klimt, Munch, Matisse, Picasso, Léger, Archipenko, Moholy-Nagy, Pevsner, Lipchitz, Gonzalez, Klee, Kandinsky, Marc, Nolde, Kokoschka,

Barlach, Schwitters, Arp, Ernst, Miró, Giacometti, Rouault, Moore, Armitage, Chadwick, Poliakoff, Mathieu, Vasarely, Dubuffet, Matta, Tobey, Calder, Lehmden, Wagemaker, Wines, among many others; also collections of photographs, films and architectural designs.

Hours: Closed Wednesday; open Sunday, 10–1; Friday, 2–9; other days, 10–4.

Admission: 10 schillings; students, 1 schilling.

• MUSEUM FUR ANGEWANDTE KUNST (Museum of Applied Arts), Stubenring 5, Tel: 72 56 96. Collections of glass, textiles, furniture, ceramics, metalwork.

Hours: Closed Monday; open Sunday, 9–1; other days, 9–4.

Admission: October 1–March 31, Sunday and holidays, free; other times: 5 schillings; students, free.

• NIEDEROSTERREICHISCHES LANDESMUSEUM (Museum of Lower Austria), Herrengasse 9, Tel: 63 57 11. Works by artists of the Province of Lower Austria including Kokoschka, Schiele, Dobrowsky and others.

Hours: Closed Monday; open Sunday, 9–1; other days, 9–5.

Admission: 1 schilling.

• OSTERREICHISCHE GALERIE DES 19. UND 20. JAHRHUNDERTS, Oberes Belvedere, Prinz-Eugen-Strasse 27, Tel: 72 64 21. Collection of 19 and 20 century Austrian painting and sculpture including works by Klimt, Böckl, Schiele, Kokoschka and others.

Hours: Closed Monday; open Sunday and holidays, 9–1; other days, 10–4.

Admission: October 1–March 31, Sunday and holidays, free; other times: 5 schillings; students, free.

Publications:

Alte und Moderne Kunst, monthly illustrated magazine of Austrian art, crafts and architecture, published by RZR-Verlag, Neuermarkt 1, Vienna.

Open Air Museum of Sculpture Middelheim, Antwerp

BELGIUM

Antwerp [*Anvers*]

• Koninklijk Museum voor Schone Kunsten (Musée Royal des Beaux-Arts), Leopold de Waelplaats, Tel: 37 06 36. Collection includes works of 19 and 20 centuries, primarily Belgian with, among others, Ensor, de Smet, Permeke, van Dongen, Zadkine, Utrillo, Vlaminck, Despiau, Dufy.

Hours: Closed Tuesday; open other days: April 15–September 30, 10–5; October 1–November 14, 10–4; November 15–January 15, 10–3; January 16–April 14, 10–4.

Admission: Sunday all day and Wednesday and Saturday after 1, free; other times, 5 francs.

• Openluchtmuseum voor Beeldhouwkunst (Open Air Museum of Sculpture), Middelheim Park, Middelheimlaan 61, Tel: 38 11 82. Collection of modern sculpture exhibited in a large garden; also biennial exhibitions of modern sculpture.

Hours: Daily, 10–sunset.

Admission: Free, except during Biennales.

Bruges [*Brugge*]

• MUSEUM BRANGWYN (of the Stedelijke Musea), Dyver 16, Tel: 3 61 33. Contains extensive collection of paintings and prints by English artist Frank Brangwyn (1867–1956).

Hours: Daily: April 1–September 30, 9:30–12 and 2–6; October 1–March 31, 10–12 and 2–4.

Admission: 5 francs.

Brussels [*Bruxelles*]

• MUSEE D'ART MODERNE (of Musées Royaux des Beaux-Arts de Belgique), place Royale. Includes works by Seurat, Gauguin, Ensor, Wouters, Matisse, Zadkine, Moore, Richier, among others.

Hours: Closed Monday and January 1, November 11 and afternoon of November 1; open other days: February 16–November 15, 10–5; November 16–February 15, 10–4.

Admission: Free.

• MUSEE DES BEAUX-ARTS D'IXELLES, 71 rue Jean van Volsem, Tel: 11 90 84. Includes works by impressionists and post-impressionists.

Hours: Closed Monday, holidays and Sunday after 1; open other days: April 1–September 30, 10–5; October 1–March 31, 10–4.

Admission: Free.

• PALAIS DES BEAUX-ARTS DE BRUXELLES, 23 rue Ravenstein, Tel: 12 10 03. Contains exhibition hall where frequent major loan exhibitions of modern art are presented; also concert halls and theaters.

Ghent [*Gand*]

• MUSEE DES BEAUX-ARTS, parc de la Citadelle, Tel: 22 17 03. Includes modern painting, sculpture, drawings and tapestries.

Hours: Daily: April 1–September 30, 10–12:30 and 2–6; October 1–March 31, 10–12 and 2–4 (closed Sunday afternoon, October 1–March 31).

Admission: 5 francs.

Liège

• MUSEE DE L'ART WALLON, 7 parc de la Boverie, Tel: 43 04 03. Section of 19 and 20 century art by Walloon artists including Rops, de Witte, Delvaux, Magritte and a large collection of works by Auguste Donnay.

Hours: Closed Wednesday; open other days: April 1–September 30, 10–1 and 2:30–6:30; October 1–March 31, 10–1 and 2:30–4:30.

Admission: Free.

• MUSEE DES BEAUX-ARTS, 34 rue de l'Académie, Tel: 32 07 99. Contains paintings and sculpture by North Belgian and foreign artists including the country's most complete collection of modern French art.

Hours: Closed Friday; open other days: April 1–September 30, 10–1 and 2:30–6:30; October 1–March 31, 10–1 and 2:30–4:30.

Admission: Free.

Tournai

• MUSEE DES BEAUX-ARTS, enclos St. Martin. Contains works by several major artists including Manet, Monet, van Gogh, Seurat.

Hours: April 1–September 30, daily, 9:30–1 and 2–6; October 1–March 31, Sunday and holidays only, 10–12 and 2–4.

Admission: 5 francs.

Publications:

• *Les Beaux-Arts,* 10 rue Royale, Brussels, published weekly.

National Art Gallery, Sofia

BULGARIA

Bourgas

• THE ART GALLERY. Contains sculpture, painting and prints of 20 century including works by Vladimir Dimitrov, Iliya Petrov, Alexander Stamenov, Dechko Ouzounov, Georgi Bayev and others.

Hours: Daily, 10–12 and 3–7.

Kazanluk
• ART GALLERY OF THE ISKRA NATIONAL MUSEUM. Contains 400 works by Bulgarian painters and sculptors including Anton Mitov, Stefan Ivanov, Tseno Todorov, Iliya Petrov, Ivan Mandov and others, also works by foreign artists.

Hours: Daily, 9–12 and 3–6.
Admission: Free.

Plovdiv
• STATE ART GALLERY, 15 Vassil Kolarov Street. Primarily Bulgarian art of 19 and 20 centuries including works by Stanislav Dospevski, Nikolai Pavlovich, Georgi Danchov, Ivan Angelov, Nikola Petrov and others, also department of foreign art.

Hours: Tuesday, Wednesday, Thursday, Saturday and
       Sunday, 9–7.
Admission: Free.

Roussé
• THE ART GALLERY, 6 Sredets Street. Includes 20 century works by Vladimir Dimitrov, Dechko Ouzounov, Bencho Obreshkov, Boris Ivanov, Georgi Bayev and others.

Hours: Sunday, Monday, Wednesday, Thursday and
       Saturday, 10–12 and 3–7.
Admission: Free.

Sofia
• NATIONAL ART GALLERY, 6 Moskovska Street, Tel: 7 00 86. Bulgarian and foreign painting, sculpture, prints, drawings and icons of 19 and 20 centuries including works by Cézanne, Renoir, Carrà, Chagall, Pascin, Picasso and others.

Hours: Closed Tuesday; open Monday, 9–2; other days,
       10–6.
Admission: Adults, 8 stotinki; children and groups, 4
       stotinki.

Interior, Národní Galerie, Prague

CZECHOSLOVAKIA

Prague [*Praha*]

• NARODNI GALERIE (National Gallery), Hradčanské náměstí 15, Hradcany, Tel: 628 67. Includes 19 and 20 century painting, sculpture, prints and drawings by European artists, among whom are Daumier, Corot, Monticelli, the impressionists, Gauguin, van Gogh, Toulouse-Lautrec, Signac, Dufy, Matisse, Utrillo, Picasso, Chagall.

Hours: Closed Monday; open other days, 10–6.

• SBIRKA MODERNIHO UMENI (Collection of Modern Art), Budova Městské Lidové Knihovny (Municipal Library Building), náměstí Dr. V. Vacka 1, Staré Město. Czech and Slovak painting of the 20 century; also temporary exhibitions of Czech and foreign contemporary art.

Hours: Closed Monday; open other days, 10–6.

• UMELECKO PRUMYSLOVE MUSEUM (Museum of Arts and Crafts), Ulice 17, Listopadu 2. Includes furniture, glass and ceramics of 19 and 20 centuries.

Zbraslav

• NARODNI GALERIE (National Gallery), Castle. Includes collection of Czech sculpture.

Hours: Closed Monday; open other days, 10–6.

Publications:

Panorama, magazine published by the Friends of the Plastic and Graphic Arts, Besední 3, Prague.

Louisiana Museum, Humlebaek

DENMARK

Copenhagen [København]

• DANSKE KUNSTINDUSTRIMUSEET (Danish Museum of Decorative Art), Bredgade 68, Tel: Central 94 52. Includes contemporary Asian and European arts and crafts.
Hours: Daily, 1–4.
Admission: Free.

• HIRSCHSPRUNGSKE SAMLING (Hirschsprung Collection), Stockholmsgade 20, Tel: Obro 6 33. Private collection of 19 century Danish art.
Hours: Closed Monday; open other days: April 1–

October 14, 2–5; October 15–March 31, 2–4, also
Tuesday and Friday evenings, 7–9.

Admission: Free.

• NY CARLSBERG GLYPTOTEK, Dantes Plads, Tel:
Byen 10 65. Includes 19 and early 20 century Danish and
French painting and sculpture with works by, among
others, Manet, Cézanne, Degas, Sisley, Renoir, Maillol,
Bonnard, Toulouse-Lautrec and 25 paintings by Gauguin.

Hours: Daily: May 1–June 14, 10–4; June 15–September 14, 10–5; September 15–October 31, 10–4;
November 1–April 30, 1–3 (except Sunday,
11–3).

Admission: Adults: Wednesday and Sunday, free; other
days, 2 kroner; children: free every day.

• ORDRUPGAARDSAMLINGEN (Ordrupgaard Collection), Vilvordevej 110, Charlottenlund, Tel: OR 11 83.
Private collection of 19 century French art.

Hours: May 1–September 30, Wednesday, Saturday and
Sunday, 2–5; October 1–April 30, Saturday and
Sunday, 2–4.

Admission: Adults, 1 krone; children, free.

• STATENS MUSEUM FOR KUNST (State Art Gallery), Sølvgade, Tel: Palae 19 16. Contains 19 and 20
century Scandinavian art and the J. Rumps Collection
including Maillol, Utrillo, Vlaminck, Laurens, Derain,
Gris, Rouault, Modigliani, Dufy, Braque, Picasso and 24
works by Matisse.

Hours: Closed Monday; open April 1–September 30:
Tuesday–Sunday, 10–5; October 1–March 31:
Tuesday–Friday, 10–3; Saturday and Sunday,
10–4.

Admission: Free.

Dronningmølle [*near Hornbaek*]

• RUDOLPH TEGNER MUSEUM, Hildekrog. Sculpture and painting by Tegner (1873–1950) including 14 bronzes exhibited in park.

Hours: Daily, 9–12 and 2–sunset.

Admission: Adults, 1 krone; children, 0.50 krone.

Faaborg

• MUSEUM FOR FYNSK MALERKUNST, Grønnegade, Tel: 3 41. Contains paintings by a group of turn-of-the-century Danish artists from the island of Fyn, also sculpture by Kai Nielsen.

Hours: Daily: April 1–September 30, 10–12 and 1:30–5; October 1–March 31, 10–12 and 1:30–4.

Admission: Sunday, 1:30–4, free; other times, 1 krone.

Frederikssund

• J. F. WILLUMSEN MUSEUM, Jenriksvej, Tel: 7 73. Contains works by the artist Jens Ferdinand Willumsen (1863–1958), as well as his personal collection.

Hours: Sunday, 10–5; other days, 10–12 and 2–5.

Admission: Adults, 1.50 kroner; children, 1 krone.

Humlebaek

• LOUISIANA MUSEUM, Gl. Strandvej 13, Tel: 7 19. Located on an estate 20 miles north of Copenhagen on the shores of the Oresund. Collection of 20 century Danish painting, sculpture and crafts; loan exhibitions, dramatic performances, concerts, recitals, lectures and films are included in the seasonal program.

Hours: Daily: June 1–August 31, 10–9; September 1–May 31, 10–5.

Admission: 3 kroner.

Publications:

Dansk Kunsthaandvaerk, published ten times a year by Danish Society of Arts and Crafts and Industrial Design, Bredgade 66, Copenhagen.

Coming Events in Denmark, published by National Travel Association of Denmark, Banegaardspladsen 5–7, Copenhagen, lists current art exhibitions.

Tate Gallery, London

ENGLAND

National Gallery, London

Bedford

• Cecil Higgins Museum, Castle Close, Tel: 3791. Collection includes English watercolors and drawings of 19 and 20 centuries and some small sculpture.

Hours: Closed Good Friday and December 25; open Sunday, 2:30–5; other days, 11–6 (closes at dusk, October–March).

Admission: Free.

Berwick-on-Tweed [*Northumberland*]

• BERWICK-ON-TWEED MUSEUM AND ART GALLERY, Marygate, Tel: 7320. Collection of paintings, given to the gallery by the late Sir William Burrell, includes works by Daubigny, Boudin and Degas.

Hours: Closed Sunday; open other days, 10–7.

Admission: Free.

Birmingham

• BARBER INSTITUTE OF FINE ARTS, The University, Tel: SEL 0962. Contains works by Courbet, Manet, Pissarro, Monet, Degas, Gauguin and Toulouse-Lautrec.

Hours: Open first Saturday each month, 10–4; Wednesday (except in week in which first Saturday falls), 12–5; also weekdays by application.

Admission: Free.

• BIRMINGHAM CITY MUSEUM AND ART GALLERY, Congreve Street, Tel: CEN 7000. Collection of Pre-Raphaelite paintings and drawings, also a number of 19 century French paintings, contemporary English paintings and a small sculpture collection which includes bronzes by Rodin, Renoir, Epstein, Moore and others.

Hours: Sunday, 2–5:30; other days, 10–6.

Admission: Free.

Bradford [*Yorkshire*]

• CITY ART GALLERY AND MUSEUM, Cartwright Memorial Hall, Tel: 4135. Includes English painting and drawings of 19 and 20 centuries.

Hours: Daily: May–August, 10–8; April and September,

10–7; January–March and October–December, 10–5.

Admission: Free.

Brighton [*Sussex*]
• BRIGHTON ART GALLERY AND MUSEUM, North-gate House, Church Street, Tel: 63005. Includes modern watercolors, prints and drawings.

Hours: Sunday, 2–7 (winter, 2–6); other days, 10–7.
Admission: Free.

Bristol [*Gloucestershire*]
• BRISTOL CITY ART GALLERY, Queen's Road, Tel: 25908. Contains two rooms of contemporary painting and sculpture.

Hours: Closed Sunday; open other days, 10–6.
Admission: Free.

Cambridge
• ARTS COUNCIL GALLERY, 2 All Saints' Passage, Tel: 53165. Periodically presents modern art exhibitions.

Hours: Closed Sunday; open other days, 11–6.
Admission: Free.

• FITZWILLIAM MUSEUM, Trumpington Street, Tel: 50023. Includes 19 and 20 century British and French art with, among others, works by the Pre-Raphaelites and a bronze head of Einstein by Epstein.

Hours: Closed first Wednesday of each month; open Sunday (picture galleries only), 2–5 (September–April, 2–4); other days, 10–5 (September–April, 10–4).

Admission: Free.

Cookham-on-Thames [*Berkshire*]
• STANLEY SPENCER GALLERY, King's Hall. Collection of works by the artist Sir Stanley Spencer (1891-1959) on permanent exhibition; also frequent temporary loan exhibitions of his work.

Hours: April–September, daily, 10:30–7:30.
Admission: Adults, 2 shillings; children and students, 1 shilling.

Coventry [*Warwickshire*]

· HERBERT ART GALLERY AND MUSEUM, Jordan Well, Tel: 20631/5. Primarily devoted to temporary loan exhibitions; Art Gallery does, however, contain collection of modern British figurative painting and sculpture with emphasis on local artists.

Hours: Sunday, 2–5; Tuesday and Wednesday, 10–8; other days, 10–6.
Admission: Free.

Eastbourne [*Sussex*]

· THE TOWNER ART GALLERY, Manor House, 9 Borough Lane, Tel: 1635. Collection includes modern painting and prints; frequent temporary loan exhibitions.

Hours: Sunday, 3–5; other days: April–September, 10–6; October–March, 10–5.
Admission: Free.

Huddersfield [*Yorkshire*]

· HUDDERSFIELD ART GALLERY, Ramsden Street, Tel: 1956. Collection includes painting, sculpture and drawings by Charles Conder, Sickert, Epstein, Grant, David Jones, Spencer, Bratby; also frequent temporary loan exhibitions.

Hours: Closed Sunday; open Friday, 10–7:30; other days, 10–5:30.
Admission: Free.

Leeds [*Yorkshire*]

· CITY ART GALLERY, Municipal Buildings, Calverley Street, Tel: 26609. Collection includes 19 and 20 century British and French painting, sculpture, prints and drawings; also frequent loan exhibitions.

Hours: Sunday, 2:30–5; other days, 10:30–6:30.
Admission: Free.

Leicester
• LEICESTER MUSEUM AND ART GALLERY, The New Walk, Tel: 56081. Includes works by British modern artists and a collection of paintings by German expressionists; also frequent temporary exhibitions.

Hours: Sunday, 2–5; other days: May–August, 10–7; April and September, 10–6; October–March, 10–5.

Admission: Free.

Liverpool
• WALKER ART GALLERY, William Brown Street, Tel: NOR 1371. Collection includes paintings by 19 and 20 century artists, among others, Courbet, Seurat, Sickert, John, Spencer, Pasmore, Bratby and sculpture by Rodin, Renoir, Epstein; also loan exhibitions of modern art.

Hours: Closed December 26; open Sunday, 2–5; other days: April–September, 10–6; October–March, 10–5.

Admission: Free.

London
• ARTS COUNCIL OF GREAT BRITAIN, 4 St. James's Square, Tel: WHI 9737. Temporary exhibitions of British and foreign art; exhibitions organized by the Council are frequently shown in the Tate Gallery.

Hours: Closed Sunday; open Tuesday and Thursday, 10–8; other days, 10–6.

Admission: Free.

• COURTAULD INSTITUTE GALLERIES, Woburn Square, Tel: LAN 1015. Includes the Samuel Courtauld Collection of important impressionist and post-impressionist paintings with works by Manet, Cézanne, Monet, Renoir, Degas, Gauguin, van Gogh, among others.

Hours: Sunday, 2–5; other days, 10–5.

Admission: Free.

• INSTITUTE OF CONTEMPORARY ARTS, 17-18 Dover Street, Tel: GRO 6186. Temporary exhibitions of contemporary art.

Hours: Gallery closed Sunday; open Saturday, 10–1; other days, 10–6.

Admission: 1 shilling.

• NATIONAL GALLERY, Trafalgar Square, Tel: WHI 7618. Contains national collection of painting of principal European schools up to and including the impressionists with works by Manet, Degas, Pissarro, Cézanne, Monet and Renoir.

Hours: Closed Good Friday, December 24 and 25; open Sunday, 2–6; other days, 10–6.

Admission: Free.

• ROYAL ACADEMY OF ARTS, Burlington House, Piccadilly, Tel: REG 7981. "Annual Summer Exhibition" of painting, sculpture, architecture and prints by living artists, May–August.

Hours: Summer: Sunday, 2–6; other days, 9:30–7; winter: Sunday, 2–6; other days, 10–7.

Admission: Free.

• SOUTH LONDON ART GALLERY, Peckham Road, Camberwell, Tel: ROD 6120. Contains small collection of contemporary British painting (may be seen by appointment only) and a reference collection of 20 century prints; also frequent loan exhibitions.

Hours: Sunday, 3–6; other days, 10–6 (print collection, Monday–Friday only, 10–5).

Admission: Free.

• TATE GALLERY, Millbank, Tel: TAT 4444. Contains the national collection of British painting, the national collection of foreign painting and drawings beginning with the impressionists and the national collection of sculpture from late 19 century to the present; included

Salford [*Lancashire*]

• CITY ART GALLERY, The Crescent, Peel Park, Tel: PEN 2649. Includes collection of works by Laurence Stephen Lowry (born 1887).

Hours: Closed January 1, Good Friday, December 25 and 26; open Sunday, 2–5; other days, 10–6 (winter, 10–5).

Admission: Free.

Sheffield [*Yorkshire*]

• GRAVES ART GALLERY, Surrey Street, Tel: 22624. Among the artists represented in the painting collection are Whistler, Sickert, Epstein and Paul Nash.

Hours: Sunday, 2–5; other days, 10–8.

Admission: Free.

Southampton [*Hampshire*]

• SOUTHAMPTON ART GALLERY, Civic Centre, Tel: 23855. Collection emphasizes British contemporary painting, also some French works of 19 and 20 centuries, including, among others, Corot, Rodin, Degas, Pissarro, Maillol, Utrillo, Sickert, John, Epstein, Spencer, M. Smith, Paul Nash, Sutherland, Pasmore, Bratby.

Hours: Sunday, 2–5; other days, 10–7.

Admission: Free.

Southport [*Lancashire*]

• ATKINSON ART GALLERY, Lord Street, Tel: 5523. Painting and sculpture, predominantly British, with works by Orpen, W. R. Flint, Sickert, Brangwyn, Fry and others.

Hours: Sunday, 2:30–5; other days, 10–7 (winter, 10–5).

Admission: Free.

Stockport [*Cheshire*]

• WAR MEMORIAL ART GALLERY, Wellington Road South, Tel: STO 4940. Contains Epstein head of Yehudi Menuhin and works by other British artists.

Hours: Saturday, 10–12 and 2–6; Sunday, 2–5; other
days, 1–7.
Admission: Free.

Stoke-on-Trent [*Staffordshire*]
• CITY MUSEUM AND ART GALLERY, Broad Street,
Hanley, Tel: 22714. Includes modern painting, sculpture
and prints.
Hours: Saturday, 10–7; Sunday, 2:30–5; other days,
10–6.
Admission: Free.

Wakefield [*Yorkshire*]
• CITY ART GALLERY, Wentworth Terrace, Tel:
2818. Painting, sculpture, prints and drawings, with em-
phasis on 20 century, including works by F. S. Gore, Gil-
man, Sickert, Epstein, Moore, Hepworth, Paul Nash,
Sutherland, Pasmore, Piper, Butler and others.
Hours: Sunday, 2:30–5:30; other days, 11–6.
Admission: Free.

York
• CITY OF YORK ART GALLERY, Exhibition
Square, Tel: 23839. Extensive collection of 19 and 20
century English painting with works by Sickert, P. W.
Steer, L. S. Lowry, Paul Nash, M. Smith, Piper and
others.
Hours: Sunday, 2:30–5; other days, 10–5.
Admission: Free.

Publications:
The Arts Review, 54 Paddington Street, London,
published fortnightly and available at bookstalls on alter-
nate Saturdays, 1 shilling.

Art Gallery Monthly Guide, published by Art
Exhibitions Bureau, 6½ Suffolk Street, Pall Mall East,
London.

Sunday newspapers, *The Observer* and *The Sunday Times,* list current exhibitions in commercial galleries.

FINLAND

Helsinki
• ATENEUMIN TAIDEMUSEO (Atheneum Art Museum), Kaivokatu 2, Tel: 62 42 40. Collection includes painting and sculpture of the 19 and 20 centuries with works by Daumier, Rodin, Corot, Daubigny, Cézanne, Munch, Sisley, Degas, Renoir, Signac, Gauguin, van Gogh, Bonnard, Dufy, Vlaminck, Rouault, Léger, Modigliani, Campigli, Afro, Manzù, Marini as well as Finnish artists; also temporary exhibitions of modern art.
Hours: Closed Monday; open other days, 10–5.

Publications:
Daily newspapers, especially Sunday editions, list exhibitions in commercial galleries.

Sisley: The Church of Moret. Musée des Beaux-Arts, Rouen

FRANCE

Musée Toulouse-Lautrec of the Musée d'Albi

Agen [*Lot-et-Garonne*]
• Musee Municipal, place de l'Hôtel de Ville, Tel: 0 27. Collection includes some works by impressionists.

Hours: Closed Tuesday and November 1, December 25; open other days, 10–12 and 2–6 (winter, 2–4).

Admission: Adults, 0.50 franc; children and groups, free.

Aix-en-Provence [*Bouches-du-Rhône*]
• Musee du Pavillon de Vendome (or Musée Dobler), 32 rue Cellony, Tel: 24 94. No modern collection, but temporary loan exhibitions of modern art are occasionally presented.

Hours: Closed Monday and public holidays; open other days: summer, 10–12 and 2–6; winter, 10–12 and 2–5.

Admission: Sunday afternoon, free; other times, 0.50 franc; also free Thursday for students.

• Musee Granet, place Saint Jean de Malte, Tel: 9 06. Painting collection includes three Cézanne watercolors.

Hours: Closed Tuesday, Easter Sunday and December 25; open other days: March 1–October 31, 9–12 and 2–6; November 1–April 30, 9–12 and 2–5.

Admission: Sunday afternoon, free; other times: 0.50 franc; students and soldiers, 0.20 franc.

Aix-les-Bains [*Savoie*]
• Musee du Docteur Faure, Villa des Chimères, boulevard des Côtes, Tel: 6 57. Faure Collection includes pre-impressionist and impressionist paintings by Jongkind, Renoir, Degas, Pissarro, Sisley, Utrillo, Monticelli and numerous works by Rodin.

Hours: Daily, Easter Sunday–October 31, 10–12 and 2–6.

Admission: 0.25 franc.

Albi [*Tarn*]
• MUSEE D'ALBI (including Musée Toulouse-Lautrec and l'Art Contemporain), Palais de la Berbie, place de l'Archevêche, Tel: 54 14 09. Contains 700 works by Toulouse-Lautrec including paintings, drawings, prints and posters, as well as a large collection of works by other modern artists, among whom are Gauguin, Denis, Bonnard, Vuillard, Matisse.

Hours: Daily: summer, 9–12 and 2–6; winter, 10–12 and 2–5.

Admission: 1.50 francs; students and groups, 0.50 franc.

Amiens [*Somme*]
• MUSEE DE PICARDIE, 48 rue de la République, Tel: 60 42. Contains 19 and 20 century art including murals by Puvis de Chavannes.

Hours: Closed Monday and January 1, May 1, November 1, December 25; open other days, 10–12 and 2–6.

Admission: Free.

Antibes [*Alpes-Maritimes*]
• MUSEE GRIMALDI (also called Musée Picasso), Château d'Antibes, Tel: 416 90. Includes large collection of paintings, sculpture, drawings and ceramics by Picasso.

Hours: Summer: daily, 10–12 and 3–7; winter: closed Monday; open other days, 10–12 and 3–5.

Admission: 1 franc.

Avignon [*Vaucluse*]
• MUSEE CALVET, 65 rue Joseph Vernet, Tel: 81 18 60. Includes art of 19 and 20 centuries, in particular, five paintings by Soutine.

Hours: Closed January 1, May 1, August 15, November 1 and 11, December 25; open other days: April–September, 9–12 and 2–6; October–March, 9–12 and 2–5.

Admission: Sunday, free; other days: 0.50 franc (1 franc for loan exhibitions) ; students, free.

Bagnols-sur-Cèze [*Gard*]

• MUSEE LEON ALEGRE, at the Mairie. Contains a collection of painting, prints and drawings by impressionists and other modern artists including Pissarro, Renoir, Monet, Morisot, Degas, Vuillard, Matisse, La Fresnaye.

Hours: Daily, except public holidays (Sunday on request).

Admission: 0.50 franc.

Biot [*Alpes-Maritimes*]

• MUSEE FERNAND LEGER, Tel: 4 90 78. Devoted exclusively to the works of Léger (1881–1955) : paintings, ceramics, tapestries, prints and drawings.

Hours: Daily, 10–12 and 2–5.

Bordeaux [*Gironde*]

• MUSEE DES BEAUX-ARTS, cour d'Albret, Tel: 44 72 31. Painting, sculpture, prints and drawings of the 19 and 20 centuries including works by Redon and Marquet.

Hours: Closed Tuesday; open other days : summer, 10–12 and 2–6; winter, 10–12 and 2–5.

Admission: Sunday and Thursday, free; other days, 0.50 franc.

Boulogne-sur-Mer [*Pas-de-Calais*]

• MUSEE DES BEAUX-ARTS ET D'ARCHEOLOGIE, 36 bis Grande-Rue, Tel: 0 31. Late 19 century art including works by Corot and Boudin.

Hours: Closed Tuesday all day, Wednesday and Saturday mornings, January 1, May 1, July 14, November 1 and 11, December 25; open other times, 10–12 and 2–5 :45.

Admission: Free.

Cagnes-sur-Mer [*Alpes-Maritimes*]

• MUSEE RENOIR DU SOUVENIR, in villa, Les Collettes, Tel: 233 36. Former home of Auguste Renoir (1841–1919) containing paintings and sculpture by him from the Cagnes period, 1903–1919.

Hours: Closed Tuesday and May 1; open other days, 2–6.

Admission: 1 franc.

Cambrai [*Nord*]

• MUSEE MUNCIPAL, 15 rue de l'Epée. Collection includes works by Utrillo, Vlaminck, Dufy, Matisse.

Hours: Closed Monday and month of September or October; open other days, 10–12 and 2–5.

Admission: Free.

Carcassonne [*Aude*]

• MUSEE DES BEAUX-ARTS, 1 rue de Verdun. Includes Joe Bousquet Collection of contemporary and surrealist works with, among others, Marquet, Picasso, Léger, Fautrier, Masson, Miró, Ernst.

Hours: Closed Sunday; open other days, 8–11 and 2–5.

Admission: 0.30 franc.

Céret [*Pyrénées-Orientales*]

• MUSEE D'ART MODERNE, rue Joseph Parayre, Tel: 36. Collection includes painting, sculpture, prints, drawings, ceramics by cubists as well as works by Maillol, Matisse, Marquet, Chagall and others; also illustrated books and letters by Jean Cocteau and Max Jacob.

Hours: Daily, 9–12 and 2–5 (closes at sunset in winter).

Admission: Adults, 1 franc; children, 0.50 franc.

Dieppe [*Seine-Maritime*]

• MUSEE DE DIEPPE, Vieux Château, Tel: 84 19 76. Includes French art of 19 and 20 centuries

33

with works by Courbet, Boudin, Pissarro, Sisley and others.

Hours: Closed Tuesday; open other days: March 1–October 31, 10–12 and 2–6; November 1–April 30, 10–12 and 2–5.

Admission: 0.50 franc (1 franc for special exhibitions).

Dreux [*Eure-et-Loir*]

• Musée d'Art et d'Histoire, place du Musée, Tel: 7 01. Includes modern paintings by, among others, Valtat, Chapelain-Midy, Vlaminck, Brayer.

Hours: Closed Monday, Tuesday, Wednesday, Friday and public holidays; open Thursday and Sunday, 10–12 and 2–5; Saturday, 2–5.

Admission: 0.30 franc.

Grenoble [*Isère*]

• Musée de Peinture et de Sculpture, place de Verdun, Tel: 44 62 22. One of the most extensive collections of modern art in France, it includes paintings by Monet, Gauguin, Bonnard, Vlaminck, Modigliani, Utrillo, Dufy, Matisse, Braque, Picasso and many others.

Hours: Closed Tuesday and public holidays (except Easter Monday and Whitmonday); open other days: Easter Sunday–October 31, 9–12 and 2–5; November 1–Easter Sunday, 10–12 and 2–5.

Admission: Sunday afternoon, free; other times: summer, 0.50 franc; winter, 0.30 franc.

• Musée Fantin-Latour (annex of the Musée de Peinture et de Sculpture), 1 rue Général de Beylié, Tel: 44 76 12. Contains the drawing collection of the museum.

Hours: Closed Tuesday and public holidays (except Easter Monday and Whitmonday); open other days: Easter Sunday–October 31, 9–12 and 2–5; November 1–Easter Sunday, 10–12 and 2–5.

Honfleur [*Calvados*]

• MUSÉE DES BEAUX-ARTS, rue Albert Ier, Tel: 3 03. Collection includes impressionists and other artists of late 19 and 20 centuries with works by Friesz, Marquet, Dufy, Villon and 60 works by Boudin.

Hours: Closed Monday (except Easter Monday and Whitmonday) ; open other days, Easter Sunday–October 15, 10–12 and 2–6.

Admission: 0.50 franc; artists and soldiers, free.

Le Cateau [*Nord*]

• MUSÉE HENRI MATISSE ET HERBIN, Hôtel de Ville, Tel: 10. Paintings, sculpture, prints and illustrated books given by Matisse to his birthplace, as well as drawings by Gromaire and works by Auguste Herbin, who also lived in Le Cateau.

Hours: Thursday, Saturday, Sunday and public holidays, 3–6.

Admission: 0.50 franc.

Le Havre [*Seine-Maritime*]

• MUSÉE DES BEAUX-ARTS DU HAVRE. Opened in 1961, museum includes works by Corot, Renoir, Monet, Braque, Dufy, Matisse and 295 paintings by Boudin, as well as contemporary tapestries.

Hours: Closed Tuesday; open other days: March 16–October 1, 10–12 and 2–7; October 2–October 15, 10–12 and 2–6; October 16–March 15, 10–12 and 2–5.

Lille [*Nord*]

• PALAIS DES BEAUX-ARTS, place de la République, Tel: 57 01 84. Collection includes paintings and drawings by the impressionists and other 19 century artists, among them, Courbet, Corot, Millet, Boudin and Monet.

Hours: Closed Tuesday and January 1, May 1, November 1, December 25; open other days, 10–12:30 and 2–5.

Limoges [*Haute-Vienne*]

• MUSEE MUNICIPAL, place de la Cathédrale, Tel: 59 51. Includes modern drawings.

Hours: Closed Tuesday (except in July and August); open other days: May 1–September 30, 10–12 and 2–6; October 1–April 30, 10–12 and 2–5.

Admission: Free (except during special exhibitions).

Lyon [*Rhône*]

• MUSEE DES BEAUX-ARTS, Palais Saint Pierre, 20 place des Terreaux, Tel: 28 07 66. Extensive collection includes art of 19 and 20 centuries with works by impressionists and Daumier, Rodin, Despiau, Zadkine.

Hours: Closed January 1, May 1, July 14, November 1 and 11, December 25; open other days, 10–12 and 2–6.

Admission: Sunday, free; other days, 0.50 franc.

Marseilles [*Bouches-du-Rhône*]

• MUSEE CANTINI, 19 rue Grignan, Tel: 37 86 33. Contains modern painting and sculpture including works by Marquet, Dufy, Rouault.

Hours: Closed Tuesday all day, Friday morning and May 1, July 14, November 11, December 25; open other days: April 1–September 30, 9–12 and 3–6; October 1–March 31, 9–12 and 2–5.

Admission: Sunday morning, free; other times, 0.50 franc; students and soldiers, free.

• MUSEE DES BEAUX-ARTS, Palais Longchamp, Tel: 62 21 17. Includes works by Puvis de Chavannes, Monticelli and a Daumier collection.

Hours: Closed Tuesday all day, Friday morning and May 1, July 14, November 11, December 25; open other days: April 1–September 30, 9–12 and 3–6; October 1–March 31, 9–12 and 2–5.

Admission: Sunday morning, free; other times, 0.50 franc; students and soldiers, free.

Martigues [*Bouches-du-Rhône*]
• GALERIE ZIEM, in Musée du Vieux-Martigues, rue du Colonel Denfert. Paintings and personal mementos of the painter Félix Ziem (1821–1911).

Hours: July–September, daily, 10–12 and 2–6; October–June, Thursday, Sunday and public holidays, 10–12 and 2–6.

Admission: 0.30 franc.

Menton [*Alpes-Maritimes*]
• MUSEE MUNICIPAL, rue Lorédan-Larchey. Includes Charles Wakefield Mori Collection of 20 century art with works by Valadon, Utrillo, Modigliani, Soutine, Kisling, Dufy, Chagall, Picasso and others.

Hours: Closed Monday and public holidays; open other days: summer, 9–12 and 3–6; winter, 9–12 and 2–5.

Admission: 0.50 franc; students and soldiers, 0.25 franc.

Meudon [*Seine-et-Oise*]
• MUSEE RODIN (annex of Musée Rodin, Paris), Villa des Brillants, avenue Auguste Rodin, Tel: Obs. 13 09. Studies, models and sketches by Rodin.

Hours: Open only April 1–November 1, Sunday, 1–6.

Admission: 1 franc.

Montauban [*Tarn-et-Garonne*]
• MUSEE INGRES, 19 rue de Mairie, Tel: 63 18 04. Includes work by students of Ingres and David as well as a large collection of sculpture and drawings by Bourdelle.

Hours: Closed May 1; open Palm Sunday–October 15: Sunday and holidays, 10–12 and 2–5; other days, 10–12 and 2–6; October 16–eve of Palm Sunday: closed Monday and public holidays; open Sunday, 2–5; other days, 10–12 and 2–5.

Admission: Sunday and holidays, free; other days, 0.50 franc.

Montpellier [*Hérault*]

• MUSÉE FABRE, rue Montpellieret, Tel: 72 93 76. Collection includes extensive works of the 19 century by, among others, Courbet, Corot, Bazille.

Hours: Closed Monday and public holidays; open other days, 9–12 and 2–5.

Admission: Sunday and Tuesday, free; other days, 0.20 franc; students, free every day.

Nancy [*Meurthe-et-Moselle*]

• MUSÉE DES BEAUX-ARTS, 3 place Stanislas, Tel: 31 41. Art of mid-19 century with works by Courbet and Manet.

Hours: Closed Tuesday; open other days: summer, 10–12 and 2–6; winter, 10–12 and 2–5.

Admission: 0.30 franc.

Nantes [*Loire-Atlantique*]

• MUSÉE DES BEAUX-ARTS, 10 rue Georges Clémenceau, Tel: 73 17 10. Art of the 19 and 20 centuries including works by Courbet, the impressionists, Dufy, Manessier and others.

Hours: Closed Tuesday and public holidays; open other days: April 1–September 30, 9–12 and 2–6; October 1–March 31, 9–12 and 2–5.

Admission: Adults, 0.50 franc; students and children, free.

Nice [*Alpes-Maritimes*]

• MUSÉE DE L'ART ANCIEN ET MODERNE (known as Musée Chéret), 33 avenue des Baumettes, Tel: 853 18. Includes paintings by Bonnard, Vuillard, Marquet, Dufy, Derain, Matisse and works by Jules Chéret.

Hours: Closed Monday and public holidays; open other days, 10–12 and 2–6.

Admission: 0.50 franc.

• MUSEE MASSENA, promenade des Anglais and 65 rue de France, Tel: 811 34. Collection includes works by impressionists.

Hours: Closed Monday and public holidays; open óther days, 10–12 and 2–5.

Admission: Last Sunday of month, free; other days, 0.50 franc.

Nice-Cimiez [*Alpes-Maritimes*]

• MUSEE MATISSE. Opened in January 1963 in the Villa des Arènes, the museum contains 25 oils, 120 gouaches and drawings, 130 prints as well as studies, sketches and many other works by Henri Matisse (1869–1954); also furniture and personal souvenirs which belonged to him.

Hours: Open Thursday, Saturday and Sunday, 2–5.

Admission: 1.50 francs.

Paris

• BIBLIOTHEQUE NATIONALE (National Library), 58 rue de Richelieu (2ᵉ), Tel: Ric. 00 06. Largest public collection of prints in France, including modern prints and illustrated books; also special exhibitions which include modern works.

Hours: Closed Sunday and public holidays; open other days, 10–12 and 2–4.

Admission: 0.50 franc.

• MUSEE ANTOINE BOURDELLE, 16 rue Antoine Bourdelle (16ᵉ), Tel: Lit. 67 27. Former studio of the sculptor Bourdelle (1861–1930) containing extensive collection of his work including 875 pieces of sculpture, 100 paintings, 1500 drawings; also loan exhibitions of modern sculpture.

Hours: Closed Tuesday; open other days, 10–12 and 2–5.

Admission: 0.50 franc (1 franc for special exhibitions); artists and students, 0.25 franc.

• MUSEE D'ART MODERNE DE LA VILLE DE PARIS (Palais de New York), 11 avenue du Président Wilson (16e), Tel: Klé. 20 10. Some modern works on permanent exhibitions; eventually the modern works from the Petit Palais will be housed here; also temporary exhibitions.

Hours: Closed Tuesday and public holidays; open other days, 10–12 and 2–6.

• MUSEE DE L'ECOLE SUPERIEURE DES BEAUX-ARTS, 14 rue Bonaparte (6e), Tel: Lit. 50 01. Collection includes drawings of the 19 century.

Hours: Temporarily closed.

• MUSEE DE L'ORANGERIE, place de la Concorde and quai des Tuileries (1er), Tel: Opé. 82 10. Permanent installation of the "Nymphéas," murals of waterlilies by Monet, as well as temporary exhibitions.

Hours: Closed for reconstruction.

• MUSEE DES ARTS DECORATIFS, Palais du Louvre, 107 rue de Rivoli (1er), Tel: Opé. 49 68. Collection includes contemporary applied arts; loan exhibitions of modern art are presented in the Pavillon de Marsan.

Hours: Closed Tuesday and public holidays; open other days, 10–12 and 2–5.

Admission: 1 franc.

• MUSEE DU JEU DE PAUME, place de la Concorde and rue de Rivoli (1er), Tel: Opé. 12 07. Houses the Louvre's large and important collection of impressionist and post-impressionist works.

Hours: Closed Tuesday and public holidays; open other days, 10–5, also occasionally Friday evening, 9–11:30.

Admission: Sunday, free; other days, 1 franc (2 francs at night); students, 0.50 franc.

• Musée du Louvre, Porte Denon, place du Carrousel (1er), Tel: Opé. 82 10. Includes 19 century painting, prints and drawings with works by Daumier, Corot, Courbet, Monticelli, Millet, among others. The Louvre prints its own editions of many 19 and 20 century original etchings, engravings and lithographs, which are for sale in the Chalcographie du Louvre.

Hours: Closed Tuesday, legal holidays (except Easter Monday, Whitmonday and August 15 if it falls on a Sunday); open other days, 10–5.

Admission: Sunday, free; other days, 1 franc; students, 0.50 franc.

• Musée du Petit Palais (or Musée des Beaux-Arts de la Ville de Paris), avenue Alexandre III (8e), Tel: Anj. 99 21. Includes 19 and 20 century art with works by Courbet, Redon, Vuillard, Bonnard, Rouault, among others.

Hours: Closed Tuesday and public holidays; open other days, 10–5.

Admission: Sunday, free; other days, 0.50 franc.

• Musée Galliera, 10 avenue Pierre Ier de Serbie and avenue du Président Wilson (16e), Tel: Pas. 96 85. Temporary exhibitions of modern art.

Hours: Closed Tuesday; open other days, 10–6.

• Musée Gustave Moreau, 14 rue de la Rochefoucauld (9e). Contains paintings, drawings and sketches by Moreau (1826–1898), which were found in his studio at his death, plus some additional works by him.

Hours: Closed Sunday, Tuesday and public holidays; open other days, 10–5.

Admission: 0.30 franc.

• Musée J.-J. Henner, 43 avenue de Villiers (17e), Tel: Wag. 42 73. Contains works by the painter

Jean-Jacques Henner (1829-1905).

Hours: Closed Monday and public holidays; open other days, 2–5.

Admission: 0.50 franc.

• MUSEE MARMOTTAN, 2 rue Louis Boilly (16ᵉ), Tel: Tro. 12 80. Includes works by impressionists.

Hours: Closed July 15–September 15; open September 16–July 14, Saturday and Sunday, 2–5.

Admission: 1 franc.

• MUSEE NATIONAL D'ART MODERNE (successor to the Musée de Luxembourg), 13 avenue du Président Wilson (16ᵉ), Tel: Pas. 77 73. Painting, sculpture, drawings and tapestries, mainly French, from *c.* 1890 to the present including the fauves and cubists, with works by Bonnard, Vuillard, Valadon, Utrillo, Vlaminck, Duchamp-Villon, Delaunay, Brancusi, van Dongen, Dufy, Matisse, Braque, Picasso, Masson, Giacometti and others; also temporary exhibitions of French and foreign modern art.

Hours: Closed Tuesday and public holidays; open other days, 10–5.

Admission: Sunday, free; other days, 1 franc.

• MUSEE RODIN, 77 rue de Varenne (7ᵉ), Tel: Inv. 01 34. In the Hôtel Biron, former home of the artist, the museum contains the world's largest collection of sculpture by Auguste Rodin (1840–1917), also Rodin drawings and works from his personal collection including Carrière, Monet, Renoir, van Gogh; exhibitions of contemporary sculpture in surrounding garden.

Hours: Closed Tuesday and January 1, July 14, August 15, November 1 and 11, December 25; open other days, 1–6 (winter, 1–5).

Admission: Sunday, 0.50 franc; other days, 1 franc.

Pau [*Basses-Pyrénées*]

• MUSEE DES BEAUX-ARTS, rue Mathieu Lalanne,

Tel: 33 02. Includes art of 19 and 20 centuries with works by Boudin, Morisot, Marquet and others.

Hours: Closed Tuesday and January 1, May 1, November 1, December 25; open other days: Easter Sunday–November 1, 10–12 and 2–6; November 2–Easter Sunday, 10–12 and 2–4:30.

Admission: Sunday afternoon: 0.25 franc; students and soldiers, free; other times: 0.50 franc; students and soldiers, 0.25 franc.

Pauillac [*Gironde*]

• MUSEE DE MOUTON. Collection of Baron Philippe de Rothschild including works by Rouault, Gris, Braque, Lippold.

Hours: To be opened regularly, spring 1963.

Poitiers [*Vienne*]

• MUSEE DES BEAUX-ARTS, Hôtel de Ville, place Maréchal Leclerc, Tel: 22 07. Includes painting and sculpture of 19 and 20 centuries with works by the impressionists, Vuillard, Bonnard, Maillol, Marquet and others.

Hours: Closed Tuesday and public holidays; open other days: summer, 10–12 and 2–6; winter, 10–12 and 2–5.

Admission: 0.50 franc.

Quimper [*Finistère*]

• MUSEE DES BEAUX-ARTS, Hôtel de Ville, place Saint Corentin. Includes art of the 19 and 20 centuries with works by Corot, Boudin, Sérusier, Maufra, Marquet.

Hours: Closed Tuesday (except July 1–September 15) and public holidays; open other days: April 1–June 30, 10–12 and 2–5; July 1–September 15, 10–12 and 2–6; September 16–October 31, 10–12 and 2–5; November 1–March 31, 10–12 and 2–4:30.

Admission: July 1–September 30, 0.50 franc; October 1–June 30, 0.40 franc.

Reims [*Marne*]

• MUSEE DES BEAUX-ARTS, 8 rue Chanzy, Tel:
47 28 44. Includes works by Corot, Daubigny, Lépine,
Boudin, the impressionists and Gauguin.

Hours: Closed Tuesday and public holidays; open other
days: summer, 10–12 and 2–5; winter, 10–12 and
2–4:30.

Admission: Thursday and Sunday, free; other days, 0.30
franc.

Rennes [*Ille-et-Vilaine*]

• MUSEE DES BEAUX-ARTS, 20 quai Emile Zola,
Tel: 40 59 66. Includes impressionist and post-impressionist works.

Hours: Closed Tuesday and public holidays; open other
days, 10–12 and 2–5.

Admission: 0.50 franc; students, 0.25 franc.

Rouen [*Seine-Maritime*]

• MUSEE DES BEAUX-ARTS ET DE LA CERAMIQUE,
square Verdrel, Tel: 71 28 40. Includes works of the 19
century by Puvis de Chavannes, Millet and the impressionists.

Hours: Closed Tuesday all day, Wednesday morning
and public holidays including the last Sunday in
May; open other times: April 1–September 30,
10–12 and 2–5:30; October 1–March 31, 10–12
and 2–4.

Admission: 1 franc; students and professors, free.

Saint-Denis [*Seine*]

• MUSEE MUNICIPAL D'HISTOIRE ET D'ART DE
SAINT-DENIS, 4 place de la Légion d'Honneur, Tel: Pla.
20 40. Painting and drawings of the 19 and 20 centuries
by, among others, Manet, Guys, Signac, Pissarro, Cézanne,
Matisse, Léger and a collection of gouaches and drawings
by Picasso.

Hours: Daily, 2–6:30.

Admission: Sunday, 0.15 franc; other days, 0.30 franc; students, free.

Saint-Etienne [*Loire*]
• MUSEE D'ART ET D'INDUSTRIE, Palais des Arts, place Louis Comte, Tel: 32 64 41. Art of 19 and 20 centuries including works by Rodin, Vuillard and Matisse, prints, tapestries and posters by Toulouse-Lautrec, Steinlen and Forain.

Hours: Closed Tuesday all day, Wednesday morning and public holidays; open other times, 10–12 and 2–5.

Admission: Sunday and holidays, free; other days: adults, 0.30 franc; children under 14, free.

Saint-Paul-de-Vence [*Alpes-Maritimes*]
• AUBERGE COLOMBE D' OR, place Ormeaux. The restaurant of this country inn contains some early works by Renoir, Modigliani, Matisse, Picasso, Léger.

Saint-Tropez [*Var*]
• MUSEE DE L'ANNONCIADE, quai Saint Raphael, place Georges Grammont, Tel: 401. Important collection of modern art including many works by Signac, also Matisse, Vlaminck, Derain, Segonzac, Rouault, Braque and others.

Hours: Closed Monday; open other days: summer, 10–12 and 3–7; winter, 10–12 and 2–6.

Admission: 1 franc.

Strasbourg [*Bas-Rhin*]
• MUSEE DES BEAUX-ARTS, Château des Rohan, 2 place du Château, Tel: 35 47 27. Includes art of 19 and 20 centuries with works by Courbet, Corot, Manet, Renoir, Sisley, Pissarro, Degas and contemporary artists.

Hours: Closed Tuesday and public holidays; open other

days: June 1–September 30, 10–12 and 2–6;
October 1–March 31, 10–12 and 2–4; April 1–
May 31, 10–12 and 2–5.

Admission: Sunday morning, free; other times: adults,
0.50 franc; children and students, 0.25 franc.

Tours [*Indre-et-Loire*]
• MUSEE DES BEAUX-ARTS, 18 place François
Sicard, Tel: 41 36. Collection includes works by Degas
and Bourdelle.

Hours: Closed January 1, May 1 and 8, July 14, November 11, December 25; open other days: summer,
9–12 and 2–6; winter, 9–12 and 2–5.

Admission: 0.50 franc.

Valence [*Drôme*]
• MUSEE DES BEAUX-ARTS ET D'HISTOIRE NATURELLE, 4 place des Ormeaux, Tel: 37 81. Includes art of
19 and 20 centuries.

Hours: Closed public holidays (except Easter Sunday
and Whitsunday); open other days: February
15–October 14, 9–12 and 2–6; October 15–February 14, 9–12 and 2–5.

Admission: October 1–July 15, Thursday and Sunday
afternoons, free; other times, 0.50 franc.

Vence [*see Saint-Paul-de-Vence*]

Publications:
Cimaise, magazine of present-day art and architecture, published six times a year, 34 rue du Four, Paris.

Arts, weekly newspaper with complete exhibition calendar, 140 rue du Faubourg St. Honoré, Paris.

Expositions, Musées, Galeries, monthly (except
July, August and September are combined in one issue),
available at galleries, hotels, airline and steamship offices,
published by Comité Professionnel des Galeries d'Art, 3
rue du Faubourg St. Honoré, Paris.

Tinguely machines, Museum Haus Lange, Krefeld

WEST GERMANY

[*Including* WEST BERLIN]

Main hall, Museum Haus Lange, Krefeld

Note: The Kunstverein is an association which usually owns an art collection and regularly presents temporary modern art exhibitions.

Baden-Baden
• STAATLICHE KUNSTHALLE (Public Art Museum), Lichtentaler Allee 8a, Tel: 32 50. Temporary exhibitions of contemporary art.
Hours: Closed Monday; open other days, 10–1 and 3–6.
Admission: 1 DM.

Bamberg
• STAATSGALERIE, Neue Residenz, Tel: 8 51. Includes works by German artists of 19 and 20 centuries.
Hours: Daily, 9–12 and 2–6 (winter, 2–4).
Admission: 1 DM.

Berlin-West
• GALERIE DES 20. JAHRHUNDERTS (Gallery of the 20 Century), Jebensstrasse 2, Berlin-Charlottenburg 2, Tel: 32 51 81. Art of 20 century including German and foreign painting, sculpture, drawings and prints by, among others, Picasso, Braque, Chagall, Miró, Ernst, Arp, Gonzalez, Moore, Butler, Marini, Munch, Feininger, Barlach, Lehmbruck, Nolde, Schmidt-Rottluff, Kirchner, Kandinsky, Klee, Nay.
Hours: Closed Monday; open Sunday, 10–6; other days, 9–5.
Admission: Wednesday, free; other days, 50 pfennig.

• GEORG-KOLBE-MUSEUM, Sensburger Allee 25, Berlin-Charlottenburg 9, Tel: 94 21 44. Home and studio of German sculptor Georg Kolbe (1877–1947) containing 250 of his bronzes, sketches and drawings, as well as works by Rodin, Maillol, Corinth, Liebermann, Marcks, Pechstein, Kirchner and others.
Hours: April-September, Wednesday, Sunday and pub-

lic holidays, 10–5; October–March, Wednesday,
Sunday and public holidays, 10–3.
Admission: 1 DM.

• HAUS AM WALDSEE, Argentinische Alleè 30,
Berlin-Zehlendorf, Tel: 84 32 81. Changing exhibitions
of contemporary art.
Hours: Closed Monday; open other days, 10–6.
Admission: 50 pfennig.

• KUPFERSTICH-KABINETT, Arnimalle 23, Berlin-
Dahlem, Tel: 76 32 85. Department of Prints and Draw-
ings of the Staatliche Museen Berlin-West, including
prints of 19 and 20 centuries with works by Toulouse-
Lautrec, Corinth, Munch, Liebermann and others.
Hours: Closed Monday; open Sunday, 10–5; Wednes-
day, 9–6; other days, 9–5.
Admission: Wednesday, free; other days, 50 pfennig.

• NATIONALGALERIE (of the Staatliche Museen
Berlin-West), Schloss Charlottenburg, Luisenplatz, Berlin-Charlottenburg. German and foreign painting, sculpture and drawings from 19 century to the present including works by Manet, Monet, Renoir, Corinth, Liebermann,
the German expressionists, Hans Hartung, Manessier,
Nay, Poliakoff and others.
Hours: Closed Monday; open Sunday, 10–5; Wednesday, 9–6; other days, 9–5.
Admission: Wednesday, free; other days, 50 pfennig.

Bielefeld
• STADTISCHES KUNSTHAUS (Municipal Art Mu-
seum), Wertherstrasse 3, Tel: 6 30 01. Art of 20 century
including works by Corinth, Kollwitz, Kolbe, Marcks,
Nolde, Schmidt-Rottluff, Modigliani, Chagall, Picasso,
Léger, Arp, Miró and others.
Hours: Closed Monday; open Sunday, 10–1; other days,
11–5.
Admission: 50 pfennig.

Bochum

• STADTISCHE KUNSTGALERIE (Municipal Art Gallery), Kortumstrasse 147, Tel: 6 99 22 39. Collection of international painting, sculpture, prints and drawings from 1945 to the present.

Hours: Closed Monday; open Sunday, 10–1; other days, 10–1 and 3–6.

Bonn

• STADTISCHE KUNSTSAMMLUNGEN (Municipal Art Collections), Rathausgasse 5-7, Tel: 3 01 71. German painting, sculpture and prints of 19 and 20 centuries including works by Klee, Macke, Schmidt-Rottluff, Beckmann, Ernst, Nay and others.

Hours: Closed Monday; open Sunday, 10–1; other days, 10–1 and 3–6.

Admission: 50 pfennig.

Bremen

• KUNSTHALLE BREMEN (Bremen Art Museum), Am Wall 207. Collection includes 19 and 20 century painting, sculpture, prints and drawings by European artists, among whom are Rodin, Cézanne, van Gogh, Toulouse-Lautrec, Bonnard, Picasso, Munch, Modersohn-Becker, Beckmann, Barlach.

Hours: Closed Monday; open Saturday and Sunday, 10–2; other days, 10–4, also Tuesday and Friday evenings, 7–9.

Admission: Sunday, free; other days, 50 pfennig.

• PAULA-MODERSOHN-BECKER-HAUS (or Paula-Becker-Modersohn-Haus), Böttcherstrasse 8–10. Collection of paintings by Modersohn-Becker (1876–1907), Heinrich Vogeler and Worpswede artists.

Hours: Saturday, 10–2; Sunday, 11–1; other days, 10–4.

Admission: 50 pfennig.

Brunswick [*Braunschweig*]

• KUNSTVEREIN BRAUNSCHWEIG E. V. (Bruns-

wick Art Association), Haus Salve Hospes, Lessingplatz
12, Tel: 2 33 56.
Hours: Closed Monday; open Sunday, 10–1; other days,
10–5.
Admission: 1 DM.

Cologne [*Köln*]
• KOLNISCHER KUNSTVEREIN (Cologne Art As-
sociation), Hahnentorburg, Rudolfplatz, Tel: 23 16 21.
Hours: Closed Monday; open Sunday, 10–1; other days,
9–5.
Admission: 1 DM.

• WALLRAF-RICHARTZ-MUSEUM, MODERNE GAL-
ERIE, An der Rechtschule, Tel: 20 38 23 72. Extensive
collection of 19 and 20 century painting, sculpture and
prints with works by Renoir, Corinth, Heckel, Nolde,
Schmidt-Rottluff, Jawlensky, Klee, Kokoschka, Beckmann, Chagall, Picasso, Ernst, Soulages, Appel, Mathieu,
among many others.
Hours: Tuesday and Friday, 10–10; other days, 10–5.
Admission: 1 DM.

Constance [*Konstanz*]
• WESSENBERG-GALERIE, STADTISCHE GALERIE
(Municipal Gallery), Wessenberghaus, Wessenbergstrasse
41. Collection includes German painting and international
prints of 19 and 20 centuries.

Darmstadt
• BAUHAUS-ARCHIV, Ernst-Ludwig-Haus, Mat-
hildenhöhe. Original documents of the Bauhaus including
letters, manuscripts, photographs, sketches, drawings and
sculpture.

• HESSISCHES LANDESMUSEUM (Hessian Mu-
seum), Friedensplatz 1, Tel: 80 11. Collection includes

19 and 20 century drawings and prints, mainly by Heckel, Kirchner and Müller.

Hours: Closed Monday; open Sunday, 10–1; other days, 10–5.

Admission: Sunday, free; other days, 1 DM.

• KUNSTVEREIN DARMSTADT E. V. (Darmstadt Art Association), Kunsthalle, Steubenplatz 1, Tel: 7 19 61.

Hours: Closed Monday; open other days, 10–1 and 3–6 (winter, 2–5).

Admission: 1 DM.

Dortmund

• MUSEUM AM OSTWALL, Ostwall 7, Tel: 3 01 11. German art of the 20 century including works by Macke, Jawlensky, Kirchner, Schmidt-Rottluff, Pechstein, Nolde, Beckmann, Kokoschka and others.

Hours: Closed Monday; open Sunday, 10–1; Wednesday, 10–10; other days, 10–6.

Admission: 50 pfennig.

Duisburg

• STÄDTISCHES KUNSTMUSEUM UND LEHMBRUCK-SAMMLUNG (Municipal Art Museum and Lehmbruck Collection), Mülheimerstrasse 39, Tel: 2 81 36 30. Mainly 20 century art including painting, sculpture, drawings and prints by German expressionists, members of the *Brücke* group, the *Blaue Reiter* group and the Bauhaus. Sculpture collection includes works by Barlach, Heiliger, Mataré, Lipchitz, Laurens, Zadkine, Arp, Giacometti, Richier, Marini, Moore, Armitage, Chadwick. Also most comprehensive public collection of sculpture and other works by Wilhelm Lehmbruck (1881–1919).

Hours: Closed Monday; open Sunday, 11–1 and 3–5; other days, 9–1 and 3–6.

Admission: 50 pfennig.

Düren
• LEOPOLD-HOESCH-MUSEUM, Hoeschplatz 1, Tel:
39 11. German painting of the 20 century including works
by Corinth, Kandinsky, Jawlensky, Nolde, Kirchner,
Hofer, Beckmann, Nay, also drawings and prints of the
19 and 20 centuries.
Hours: Closed Monday; open Saturday and Sunday,
　　　　11–1; other days, 11–1 and 2:30–5.
Admission: 50 pfennig.

Düsseldorf
• KUNSTMUSEUM DER STADT DUSSELDORF (Art
Museum of the City of Düsseldorf), Ehrenhof 5, Tel:
44 67 06. Contains collection of 19 and 20 century art
including works by Lehmbruck, Archipenko, Barlach,
Mataré, Kandinsky, Klee, Marc, Jawlensky, Schmidt-
Rottluff, Nolde, Müller, Feininger, Schlemmer, Marini,
Nay and others.
Hours: Closed Monday; open Sunday, 10–1; other days,
　　　　10–5.
Admission: Free.

• KUNSTVEREIN FUR DIE RHEINLANDE UND WEST-
FALEN (Art Association of the Rhineland and West-
phalia), Kunsthalle, Alleestrasse 11a, Tel: 1 24 78.
Hours: Closed Monday; open other days, 10–5.
Admission: 1 DM.

Essen
• MUSEUM FOLKWANG, Bismarckstrasse 64-66,
Tel: 7 47 83. European painting of 19 and 20 centuries
including, among others, works by Cézanne, Renoir, Sig-
nac, van Gogh, Gauguin, Matisse, Derain, Picasso, Léger,
Mondrian, Ernst, Munch, Nolde, Kirchner, Klee, Marc,
Jawlensky, Rohlfs, Beckmann, Schlemmer, Feininger,
Baumeister and Nay; 20 century sculpture by Rodin,
Minne, Barlach, Moore, Arp and others; also drawings
and prints of 19 and 20 centuries.

Hours: Closed Monday; open other days, 10–6.
Admission: 50 pfennig.

Frankfurt a.M.
• FRANKFURTER KUNSTVEREIN (Frankfurt Art Association), Steinernes Haus, Alter Markt 44.
Hours: Daily, 10–5.
Admission: 1 DM.

• STADELSCHES KUNSTINSTITUT / STADTISCHE GALERIE (Städel Art Institute / Municipal Gallery), Schaumainkai 63, Tel: 6 18 98. Includes German and other European painting and sculpture of 19 and 20 centuries with works by Millet, Rodin, Maillol, Despiau, Manet, Monet, Cézanne, Degas, van Gogh, Rousseau, Corinth, Lehmbruck, Barlach, Kirchner, Nolde, Beckmann and others.
Hours: Sunday, 10–1; other days, 10–5 (winter, 10–4).
Admission: Sunday, free; other days, 1 DM.

Freiburg i. Br.
• KUNSTVEREIN E. V. (Art Association), Talstrasse 12.
Hours: Daily, 10–5.

Gelsenkirchen
• STADTISCHE KUNSTSAMMLUNG (Municipal Art Collection), Horster Strasse 5–7, Tel: 3 81 51/3 77. Art of the 20 century including works of the impressionists and German expressionists.
Hours: Closed Monday; open other days, 10–1 and 3–6.
Admission: Free.

Hagan
• KARL-ERNST-OSTHAUS-MUSEUM, Hochstrasse 73, Tel: 2 85 41/3 67. Art of the 20 century including works by Hodler, Macke, Kirchner, Nolde, Rohlfs, Gilles, Beckmann, Barlach, Mataré, Archipenko and others.

Hours: Closed Monday; open Sunday, 10–1; Thursday,
10–8; other days, 10–6.
Admission: 50 pfennig.

Hamburg
• ERNST-BARLACH-HAUS, Jenisch-Park. Opened
in 1963, the museum contains 60 pieces of sculpture and
several hundred drawings and prints by Barlach (1870–
1938).

• KUNSTHALLE (Art Museum), Glockengiesserwall, Tel: 24 82 51. Includes collections of 19 and 20
century art with works by Bonnard, Munch, Lehmbruck,
Kandinsky, Kirchner, Klee, Beckmann, Barlach, Kokoschka, Picasso, Chagall, Moore, Marini and others.
Hours: Closed Monday; open Wednesday, 10–8; other
days, 10–4.
Admission: 50 pfennig.

• KUNSTVEREIN IN HAMBURG (Art Association
of Hamburg), Kunsthalle, Glockengiesserwall.
Hours: Closed Monday; open other days, 10–8.
Admission: 1 DM.

Hanover
• KESTNER-GESELLSCHAFT (Kestner Society),
Warmbüchenstrasse 8, Tel: 261 42. Temporary exhibitions
of modern art.
Hours: Sunday, 10–2; other days, 10–6.

• KESTNER-MUSEUM, Trammplatz 3, Tel: 1 66
11/21 20. Collection includes 20 century prints and
drawings.
Hours: Saturday and Sunday, 10–1; Wednesday, 10–7;
other days, 10–4.
Admission: Free.

• NIEDERSACHSISCHES LANDESMUSEUM (Lower

Saxony Museum), Am Maschpark 5, Tel: 8 30 51/52. Collection includes 19 and 20 century painting, sculpture, prints and drawings by, among others, Corinth, Liebermann, Klee, Marc, Kirchner, Nolde, Kokoschka, Feininger, Heiliger, Beckmann, Picasso, Chagall, Archipenko, Laurens, Modigliani, Boccioni, de Chirico, Marini, Moore, Calder.

Hours: Saturday and Sunday, 9–2; other days, 11–4.
Admission: Free.

• WILHELM-BUSCH-MUSEUM, Georgengarten 1, Tel: 7 31 24. Most complete collection of paintings, drawings and manuscripts by the painter and illustrator Wilhelm Busch (1832–1908).

Hours: Daily, 10–6.

Heidelberg
• HEIDELBERGER KUNSTVEREIN E. V. (Heidelberg Art Association), Hauptstrasse 97.

Hours: Closed Monday; open Sunday, 10–1; other days, 10–1 and 3–5.

Kaiserslautern
• PFALZGALERIE UND GRAPHISCHE SAMMLUNG (Palatine Gallery and Print Collection), Villenstrasse 5, Tel: 29 91. Collection includes German painting, sculpture and prints of the 20 century with works by Corinth, Kirchner, Marcks, Baumeister, Winter and others.

Hours: Closed Monday; open other days, 10–12:30 and 2–4:30.
Admission: Free.

Karlsruhe
• BADISCHER KUNSTVEREIN E. V. (Baden Art Association), Waldstrasse 3.

Hours: Closed Monday; open Sunday, 11–1; other days, 10–5.
Admission: 1 DM.

• STAATLICHE KUNSTHALLE (Public Art Museum), Hans-Thoma-Strasse 2, Tel: 2 01 41. Collection includes German painting and prints of 19 and 20 centuries with works by Beckmann, Rohlfs, Klee, Marc, Kirchner, Kokoschka, among others.

Hours: Closed Monday; open other days, 10–1 and 3–5.
Admission: Free.

Kassel

• MUSEUM FRIDERICIANUM. (Administration and Documenta Gesellschaft are in the Rathaus.) "Documenta: Kunst nach 1945," international exhibition of art since 1945, is held here every four years (1959, 1963, etc.).

Kiel

• KUNSTHALLE (Art Museum), Düsternbrooker Weg 1–7, Tel: 4 00 31. Collection includes prints by European artists and German painting and sculpture of the 19 and 20 centuries with works by Corinth, Lehmbruck, Rohlfs, Nolde, Kirchner, Schmidt-Rottluff, Heckel, Barlach, Marcks and others.

Hours: Closed Monday; open other days, 10–1, also Wednesday and Saturday, 4–7.

Krefeld

• KAISER WILHELM MUSEUM, Karlsplatz 35, Tel: 63 22 69. Includes collection of modern painting, sculpture and graphic arts.

Hours: Closed Monday; open Saturday, 10–1; other days: April–August, 10–1 and 3–6; September–March, 10–5.
Admission: 50 pfennig.

• MUSEUM HAUS LANGE (of the Kaiser Wilhelm Museum), Wilhelmshofallee 91, Tel: 63 24 58. Building designed by Mies van der Rohe in 1928 as a private home, converted to museum in 1955; it contains collection of painting, sculpture, graphics and ceramics of the 20 century with works by Matisse, Picasso, Mondrian, Chagall, Léger, Man Ray, Miró, Kandinsky, Kirchner, Baumeister, Nay, Winter, Kricke, Burri, Calder, Sugai, Tàpies, Yves Klein, Tinguely and others; also frequent loan exhibitions.

Hours: Closed Monday; open Saturday, 10–1; other days: April–August, 10–1 and 3–6; September–March, 10–5.

Admission: 50 pfennig.

Leverkusen
• STADTISCHES MUSEUM (Municipal Museum), Schloss Morsbroich, Tel: 5 21 50. Collection of contemporary art including works by Kricke, Schumacher, Sugai, Corpora, Francis, Riopelle, Wagemaker and others.

Hours: Closed Monday; open other days, 10–5.

Admission: 50 pfennig.

Lübeck
• BEHNHAUS (of the Museen der Hansestadt Lübeck), Königstrasse 1. Painting and sculpture of the 19 and 20 centuries by, among others, Corinth, Maillol, Munch, Lehmbruck, Barlach, Kirchner, Kokoschka, Marcks, Wimmer.

Hours: Closed Monday; open Sunday, 11–4; other days, 10–4.

Admission: Free.

• OVERBECK-GESELLSCHAFT (Overbeck Society), Königstrasse 11.

Hours: Closed Monday; open Sunday, 11–4; other days, 10–4.

Ludwigshafen/Rhine
• STADTISCHE KUNSTSAMMLUNGEN (Municipal Art Collections), Bismarckstrasse 46, Tel: 66 61. German art of the 20 century with works by Macke, Nolde, Pechstein, Slevogt, Hofer, Beckmann, Kokoschka, Ernst, Nay and others.

Hours: Saturday and Sunday, 10–1; other days, 10–1 and 3–6.
Admission: Free.

Mannheim

• MANNHEIMER KUNSTVEREIN E. V. (Mannheim Art Association), at the Schloss.
Hours: Closed Monday; open Sunday, 10–1; other days, 10–5.

• STADTISCHE KUNSTHALLE (Municipal Art Gallery), Moltkestrasse 9, Tel: 293/24 21. Art of the 19 and 20 centuries including works by Manet, Cézanne, van Gogh, Corinth, Lehmbruck, Slevogt, Beckmann, Heiliger, Archipenko, Nay, Arp, Moore, Manessier and others.
Hours: Closed Monday; open Sunday, 10–5; other days, 10–1 and 2–5.
Admission: Free.

Marburg/Lahn

• UNIVERSITATSMUSEUM FUR KUNST UND KULTURGESCHICHTE (University Museum for Art and History of Civilization), Biegenstrasse 11, Tel: 8 11/23 52. Collection includes German painting of the 19 and 20 centuries.
Hours: Monday, 11–1; other days, 11–1 and 3–5.
Admission: 50 pfennig.

Mönchengladbach

• STADTISCHES MUSEUM (Municipal Museum), Bismarckstrasse 97, Tel: 2 57 11/336. Collection includes German art of the 20 century.
Hours: Closed Monday; open Saturday and Sunday, 10–1; other days, 10–1 and 3–5.
Admission: Free.

Mülheim/Ruhr

• STADTISCHES MUSEUM (Municipal Museum),

Leineweberstrasse 1, Tel: 44 32. Collection of German art
of the 20 century, mainly prints and watercolors, including the complete graphic work of Werner Gilles (1894–
1961) and a collection of all the early works of Otto Pan-
kok (1872–1943).
Hours: Sunday, 11–1; other days, 10–1 and 4–7.
Admission: Free.

Munich [*München*]

• NEUE PINAKOTHEK UND NEUE STAATSGALERIE
(New Picture Gallery and New Public Gallery), Haus
der Kunst, Prinzregentenstrasse 1, Tel: 22 26 51. Euro-
pean art of the 19 and 20 centuries with works by Courbet,
Corot, Manet, Corinth, Cézanne, van Gogh, Signac,
Toulouse-Lautrec, Bonnard, Vuillard, Kandinsky, Marc,
Klee, Jawlensky, Kirchner, Nolde, Schlemmer, Kokoschka,
Beckmann, Nay, de Chirico, Matisse and many others;
also temporary exhibitions.
Hours: Daily, 9–4:30.
Admission: Sunday and public holidays, free; other
days, 1 DM.

• STAATLICHE GRAPHISCHE SAMMLUNG (Public
Collection of Graphic Arts), Meiserstrasse 10, Tel:
55 82 51. Collection includes drawings and prints of 19
and 20 centuries.
Hours: Closed Saturday and Sunday; open other days,
9–5.
Admission: Free.

• STADTISCHE GALERIE UND LENBACH-GALERIE
(Municipal Gallery and Lenbach Gallery), Luisenstrasse
33, Tel: 55 00 54. Houses the Gabriele Münter Foundation
containing more than 600 paintings and drawings by
Wassily Kandinsky (1866–1944); also numerous works
by other modern artists including Klee, members of the
Blaue Reiter group and about 300 paintings and numerous drawings by Franz von Lenbach (1836–1904).

Hours: Closed Monday; open other days, 9–4:30.
Admission: Sunday and public holidays, free; other days,
50 pfennig.

Nuremberg [*Nürnberg*]
• FRANKISCHE GALERIE UND STADTISCHE KUNST-
SAMMLUNGEN (Franconian Gallery and Municipal Art
Collections), Lorenzerstrasse 32, Tel: 29 91. Collection of
German painting and sculpture of 19 and 20 centuries;
also temporary exhibitions in Fränkische Galerie.

Oberhausen/Rhineland
• STADTISCHE GALERIE (Municipal Gallery),
Schloss Oberhausen, Sterkrader Strasse, Tel: 2 46 31.
German painting and sculpture of the 20 century, also
modern graphic art.
Hours: Closed Monday; open other days, 10–5.
Admission: Free.

Offenbach/Main
• KLINGSPOR-MUSEUM, Herrnstrasse 80, Tel:
8 03 51. International center of book and printing arts of
the 20 century containing presses and special prints from
many countries; original illustrations, sketches and prints
by Corinth, Barlach, Kokoschka, Rouault, Chagall, Matisse, Picasso, Moore and others.
Hours: Saturday and Sunday, 10–12; other days, 10–12
and 3–5.
Admission: 20 pfennig.

Ratzeburg [*Kreis Lauenburg/Elbe*]
• BARLACH-GEDENKSTATTE (Barlach Memorial),
Barlachplatz 3. Collection of works by Ernst Barlach
(1870–1938) including 15 bronzes and many prints and
drawings.
Hours: Closed Monday; open other days, 10–12 and 3–5.
Admission: 50 pfennig.

Recklinghausen

• STADTISCHE KUNSTHALLE (Municipal Art Gallery), Platz am Hauptbahnhof, Tel: 2 81 41/4 76. Collection of 20 century art, mainly works by young European and American artists, and special collection of works by the *Junger Westen* group including Grochowiak, Schumacher, Götz, Meistermann, Schultze, Trier and others.

Hours: Closed Monday; open Sunday, 11–1 and 3–6; other days, 10–6.

Admission: 50 pfennig.

Saarbrücken

• SAARLAND-MUSEUM, St.-Johannes-Markt 24. Collection includes German and other European painting and sculpture of the 19 and 20 centuries.

Hours: Daily, 10–6.

Admission: Free.

Seebüll [*near Neukirchen/Schleswig, via Niebüll*]

• NOLDE-MUSEUM, STIFTUNG SEEBULL (Nolde Foundation, Seebüll), Tel: Neukirchen/Schleswig, 1 64. House built and lived in by Emil Nolde (1867–1956) containing important collection of his work including paintings, prints and ceramics as well as documentary material such as photos and letters of Nolde and others.

Hours: Open Easter–November 30, daily, 10–6.

Admission: 2 DM; students, 50 pfennig.

Soest/Westphalia

• STADTISCHE KUNSTSAMMLUNGEN (Municipal Art Collections), Rathaus, Tel: 20 56. Painting, sculpture, drawings and prints of the 20 century and extensive collection of works by Wilhelm Morgner (1891–1917) including 50 paintings and 300 prints.

Hours: Closed Sunday; open Wednesday and Saturday, 10–1; other days, 10–1 and 3–6.

Admission: 50 pfennig.

Stuttgart

• GALERIE DER STADT STUTTGART (Gallery of the City of Stuttgart), Kunstgebäude am Schlossplatz, Tel: 29 92 21. German art of the 19 and 20 centuries with about 400 works by contemporary artists, among whom are Schlemmer, Baumeister, Nesch, Ackermann, Kerkovius and Lörcher.

Hours: Closed Monday; open Saturday and Sunday, 10–4; other days, 10–6.

Admission: Free.

• KUNSTLERHAUS SONNENHALDE, Gähkopf 3, Tel: 29 77 21. Private modern art collection of Hugo Borst including works by German expressionists.

Hours: Open Saturday, 2–5.

Admission: Free.

• STAATSGALERIE STUTTGART (Stuttgart Public Gallery), Neckarstrasse 32, Tel: 2 99 72/8 95. Collection includes European art of 19 and 20 centuries with works by Cézanne, Renoir, Signac, Gauguin, Bonnard, Modigliani, Delaunay, Picasso, Chagall, Gris, Léger, Braque, Matisse, Klee, Kirchner, Feininger, Grosz, Baumeister, de Staël and others.

Hours: Closed Friday; open Tuesday and Thursday, 10–9; other days, 10–4.

Admission: Free.

Ulm/Danube

• ULMER MUSEUM, Neue Strasse 92-96, Tel: 6 16 11. Collection includes watercolors, prints and drawings by 20 century artists, among whom are Corinth, Klee, Kirchner, Picasso, Miró.

Hours: Closed Monday; open Sunday, 10–1 and 2–5; other days, 10–12 and 2–5.

Admission: 30 pfennig.

Wiesbaden

• STADTISCHES MUSEUM (Municipal Museum), Friedrich-Ebert-Allee 2, Tel: 58 61. Collection includes German painting of the 19 and 20 centuries and 20 century European sculpture, drawings and prints with works by Maillol, Lehmbruck, Jawlensky, Barlach, Beckmann, Moholy-Nagy, Nay, Götz and others.

Hours: Closed Monday; open other days, 10–5.

Admission: Free.

Witten/Ruhr

• MARKISCHES MUSEUM, Husemannstrasse 12, Tel: 32 71. Collection includes 20 century painting and prints with works by Nolde, Kirchner, Pechstein, Campendonk, Baumeister, Gilles, Bissier, Werner, Winter, Schumacher, Wagemaker and others.

Hours: Closed Monday; open Sunday, 11–1; other days, 10–1 and 2–5.

Admission: Free.

Wuppertal

• VON-DER-HEYDT-MUSEUM (formerly Städtisches Museum), Turmhof 8, Tel: 48 31. Extensive collection of 19 and 20 century art includes works by Daumier, Cézanne, Renoir, Signac, van Gogh, Munch, Modersohn-Becker, Vlaminck, Picasso, Kandinsky, Feininger, Gilles, Kokoschka, Barlach, Beckmann, Chadwick, Armitage, Calder and others.

Hours: Closed Monday; open Sunday, 10–1; Tuesday, 10–1 and 6–8; other days, 10–1 and 3–5.

Admission: 50 pfennig.

Publications:

Das Kunstwerk (The Work of Art), Agis-Verlag, Baden-Baden.

Vernissage, Agis-Verlag, Baden-Baden.

Von Atelier zu Atelier (From Studio to Studio), Progress-Verlag, Darmstadt.

Neue Schau (New View), Bärenreiter-Verlag, Kassel.

Die Weltkunst (Art of the World), Verlag Kunst und Technik, Munich.

Kulturarbeit (Cultural Work), W. Kohlhammer Verlag, Stuttgart.

GREAT BRITAIN [*see individual countries*]

HOLLAND [*see Netherlands*]

HUNGARY

Baja
• TURR ISTVAN MUZEUM, Deák Ferenc U.1.52, Tel: 2 33. Includes works by modern Hungarian painters.

Békéscsaba
• MUNKACSY MIHALY MUZEUM. Includes modern Hungarian paintings.

Budapest
• MAGYAR SZEPMUVESZETI MUZEUM (Hungarian Museum of Fine Arts), Dózsa György-ut 41, Tel: 429 759. Hungary's largest art collection, includes works of 19 and 20 century Hungarian and foreign artists, among whom are Courbet, Monet, Manet, Gauguin, Severini, Rodin, Městrović.

• MUCSARNOK (Art Gallery), Dózsa György-ut 37. Temporary exhibitions of Hungarian and foreign art.

Kaposvár
• RIPPL-RONAI MUZEUM. Includes paintings by Jozsef Rippl-Rónai (1861–1930).

ICELAND

Reykjavík

• ASGRIMSSAFN, Bergstadastraeti 74. Paintings by Asgrimur Jónsson (born 1876).

Hours: Sunday, Tuesday and Thursday, 1:30–4 and by appointment.

• ASMUNDUR SVEINSSON. Atelier containing sculpture by Sveinsson (born 1892).

Hours: By appointment.

• LISTASAFN EINARS JONSSONAR (Einar Jónsson Gallery). Contains sculpture by Jónsson (born 1874).

Hours: Sunday and Wednesday, 1:30–4.

• LISTASAFN ISLANDS (National Gallery of Iceland), Tel: 10 665. Includes modern painting and sculpture.

Hours: Sunday, Tuesday, Thursday and Saturday, 1:30–4.

NORTHERN IRELAND

Belfast
• ULSTER MUSEUM, Stranmillis, Tel: 668259. Art gallery includes contemporary painting and sculpture.

Hours: Closed Sunday; open Wednesday, 10–9; other days, 10–6.

Admission: Free.

REPUBLIC OF IRELAND

Dublin
• MUNICIPAL GALLERY OF MODERN ART, Parnell Square, Tel: 41903. Painting, sculpture and drawings of the 19 and 20 centuries including impressionist, post-impressionist, cubist, surrealist schools and works by Whistler, Sargent, Corot, Millet, Rodin, among others, as well as paintings, sculpture and stained glass by modern Irish artists; also regular temporary exhibitions.

Hours: Closed Monday; open Sunday, 11–2; Tuesday, 10:30–9; other days, 10:30–6.

Admission: Free.

Marini bronze, Peggy Guggenheim Collection, Venice

ITALY

Museo Civico, Galleria d'Arte Moderna, Turin

Agrigento [*Sicilia*]

• Museo Civico Archeologico, Piazza del Municipio 383. Includes the Galleria di Arte Moderna Giuseppe Sinatra with approximately 100 modern Italian paintings.
Hours: Daily, 9–12 and 3–6.

Alessandria [*Piemonte*]

• Museo e Pinacoteca Civica (Civic Museum and Picture Gallery), Via Tripoli 8. Includes works by Italian artists of 19 and 20 centuries.
Hours: Closed Sunday; open Saturday, 10–12; other days, 10–12 and 3–6.

Apuania Carrara [*Toscana*]

• Pinacoteca dell'Accademia di Belle Arti (Picture Gallery of the Academy of Fine Arts). Includes works by contemporary Italian artists, among whom are Tosi, Conti, Discovolo.
Hours: Apply at administrative office.

Arezzo [*Toscana*]

• Pinacoteca e Museo Medioevale e Moderno (Picture Gallery and Medieval and Modern Museum), Palazzo di Giulio III, Via San Lorentino 2. Includes painting and sculpture of the present.
Hours: Sunday, 9–1; other days, 9:30–4.

Ascoli Piceno [*Le Marche*]

• Museo Civico, Piazza del Popolo. Includes painting of the 19 century.
Hours: Summer, daily, 10–1 and 4–6; winter, daily, 8–1.

Assisi [*near Perugia, Umbria*]

• Galleria d'Arte Sacra Contemporanea (Gallery of Contemporary Religious Art), Cittadella Cristiana. Modern Italian religious art including painting, sculpture, drawings, mosaics, ceramics with works by Fazzini,

Carrà, de Chirico, Greco, Manfrini and others.
Hours: Open summer only, daily, 9–12:30 and 3–6.

Bari [*Puglia*]
• PINACOTECA PROVINCIALE (Picture Gallery of the Province), Lungomare Nazario Sauro. Includes 19 and 20 century Italian art with works by Palizzi, Toma, de Nittis and others.
Hours: Daily, 9–1.

Barletta [*Puglia*]
• MUSEO E PINACOTECA COMUNALE (Community Museum and Picture Gallery), Via Cavour 8. Includes collection of paintings by Giuseppe de Nittis (1846–1884) as well as other late 19 century Italian art.
Hours: Daily, 9–12.

Bologna [*Emilia*]
• GALLERIA COMUNALE D'ARTE MODERNA, Villa delle Rose, Via Saragozza 232. Emilian and Bolognese painting from the beginning of 20 century to the present.
Hours: In process of reorganization.

Cagliari [*Sardegna*]
• GALLERIA COMUNALE D'ARTE, Giardini Pubblici (Public Gardens). Includes works by 19 century Sardinian artists.
Hours: In process of reorganization.

Catania [*Sicilia*]
• MUSEO DI CASTELLO URSINO, Piazza Federico di Svevia. Includes 19 and 20 century painting, primarily by Sicilian artists.
Hours: Sunday, 10–12; other days, 10–2.

Faenza [*Emilia*]
• MUSEO INTERNAZIONALE DELLE CERAMICHE (International Museum of Ceramics), Via Campidori,

Tel: 67. Pottery of all periods including works by Matisse, Picasso, Chagall and contemporary Italian artists.
Hours: Sunday, 9–1; other days, 9–1 and 2:30–5:30.

Feltre [*Venezia*]
• GALLERIA D'ARTE MODERNA CARLO RIZZARDA, Via del Paradiso 8. Contains a collection of wrought-iron objects by Carlo Rizzarda (1883–1931), also works by other Italian artists of 19 and 20 centuries including Fattori, Signorini, Carrà, Morandi, Campigli, Rosai and others.
Hours: Daily, 9–12 and 2–4.

Ferrara [*Emilia*]
• MUSEO BOLDINI, Palazzo dei Diamanti, Corso Ercole d'Este 21. Contains works by the painter Giovanni Boldini (1842–1931).
Hours: Sunday, 9–12; other days, 9–12 and 3–6.

Florence [*Firenze*]
• GALLERIA NAZIONALE D'ARTE MODERNA, Palazzo Pitti, Piazza Pitti. Contains Italian painting and sculpture of 19 and 20 centuries including a collection of works by the *Macchiaioli* (Italian impressionists) as well as by Toma, Rosso, Soffici, Casorati and others.
Hours: Closed Tuesday; open Sunday, 9:30–1; other days, 9:30–4:30 (winter, 9:30–4).

Giulianova [*Abruzzi e Molise*]
• PINACOTECA BINDI (Bindi Picture Gallery), Via Garibaldi. Contains paintings by 19 century Neapolitan artists.
Hours: Apply at administrative office.

Leghorn [*Livorno*]
• MUSEO CIVICO GIOVANNI FATTORI, Villa Fabbricotti, Piazza Matteotti. Includes collection of works by

Fattori (1825-1908) and other *Macchiaioli* (Italian impressionists).

Hours: Sunday, 10–1; Thursday, 10–12:30 and 3:30–6:30; other days, 10–12:30.

Milan [*Milano*]

• GALLERIA D'ARTE MODERNA, Villa Reale, Via Palestro 16. Large collection of Italian art with works by Previati, Segantini, Rosso, de Nittis, Fattori, Lega, Signorini, Boldini, Balla, Boccioni, Morandi and others; among French artists included are Corot, Millet, Manet, Cézanne, Morisot, Renoir, Gauguin, Vuillard, Bonnard; one room is devoted to graphic art including posters by Toulouse-Lautrec; also temporary exhibitions of modern art. Nearby pavilion contains 20 century art from futurism to the present.

Hours: Closed Monday; open other days, 10–12 and 2–5.

• PINACOTECA DI BRERA (Picture Gallery of the Brera), Via Brera 28. Contains two rooms of works by 19 century Italian painters including Fattori, Hayez, Lega.

Hours: Closed Monday; open Sunday, 9:30–12:30; other days: summer, 9:30–12:30 and 2:30–5:30; winter, 10–4.

• "TRIENNALE DI MILANO," Palazzo dell' Arte al Parco, Viale Alemagna 6. International exhibition of modern decorative and industrial arts and architecture held approximately every three years (next in 1964).

Modena [*Emilia*]

• GALLERIA POLETTI, Palazzo dei Musei, Piazza Sant' Agostino 309. Includes works by local 19 century artists.

Hours: Sunday, 9:30–1; other days: summer, 9–1 and 3–6; winter, 9:30–4.

Monza [*Lombardia*]

• PINACOTECA CIVICA (Civic Picture Gallery), Palazzo Reale. Includes works by local 19 century painters, particularly Mosè Bianchi (1840–1904), and a small collection of contemporary art.

Hours: Open summer only: Saturday, 2:30–6:30; Sunday, 9–12 and 2:30–6:30.

Naples [*Napoli*]

• GALLERIA NAZIONALE DELL'ACCADEMIA DI BELLE ARTI (National Gallery of the Academy of Fine Arts), Via Bellini 36. Includes Italian and French painting of the 19 century with works by Daubigny, Corot, Mancini, Netti, Lista and others.

Hours: Apply at administrative office.

• GALLERIE NAZIONALI DI CAPODIMONTE, Palazzo di Capodimonte, Tel: 34 05 95. Includes a collection of works by 19 century Neapolitan artists with works by Toma, de Nittis, Mancini and others.

Hours: Closed Monday; open Sunday, 9:30–12:30 and 7:30–11; other days, 9:30–4.

Nervi [*near Genoa, Liguria*]

• GALLERIA CIVICA D'ARTE MODERNA, Villa Serra, Via Aldo Casotti. Contains a vast collection of 19 and 20 century Ligurian art, also works by Italian and foreign contemporary artists.

Hours: Closed Monday; open Sunday, 10–12; other days, 10–11:30 and 2–5.

Novara [*Piemonte*]

• GALLERIA GIANNONI, Palazzo del Broletto. Contains modern art including works by Bianchi, Ciardi, Gignous, Monticelli and others.

Hours: Sunday, 10–12; other days, 10–12 and 2–4.

Palermo [*Sicilia*]

• GALLERIA D'ARTE MODERNA, Politeama Gari-

baldi, Piazza Castelnuovo (entrance, Via Filippo Turati).
Includes works by 19 and 20 century artists, particularly
Sicilians, also Boldini, Sironi, Carrà, Campigli, Guttuso
and others.

Hours: Daily, 9–1.

Parma [*Emilia*]

• GALLERIA NAZIONALE, Palazzo della Pilotta,
Via della Pilotta 4. Includes paintings by 19 century local
artists.

Hours: Closed Monday; open summer: Sunday, 9–12;
other days, 9–12 and 3–6; winter: Sunday, 9–11;
other days, 9–4.

Piacenza [*Emilia*]

• GALLERIA D'ARTE MODERNA RICCI ODDI, Via
San Siro 13. Extensive collection of Italian art of the late
19 and 20 centuries including works by Rosso, Boccioni,
Carrà, Campigli and many others.

Hours: Closed Monday; open Sunday, 9:30–12:30; other
days: summer, 10–12 and 2–6; winter, 10–12
and 3–6.

Rome

• "ESPOSIZIONE NAZIONALE QUADRIENNALE
D'ARTE DI ROMA," Palazzo delle Esposizioni, Via Nazionale. Exhibition of contemporary Italian art held every
four years.

• GALLERIA NAZIONALE D'ARTE MODERNA, Viale
Belle Arti 131. Major collection of modern Italian art
with works by Segantini, Previati, Rosso, Modigliani,
Boccioni, Soffici, Severini, Carrà, de Chirico, Campigli,
Morandi, Guttuso, Marini, Manzù, Mastroianni, Afro,
Burri and many others; also includes works by foreign
artists, among whom are Klimt, Utrillo, Klee, Picasso,
van Dongen, Miró, Moore, Richier, Okada, Armitage,

Tàpies, Pollock, Tobey, Calder; also temporary exhibitions of modern art.

Hours: Closed Monday; open Sunday, 9:30–1:30; other days: summer, 9:30–1 and 3–6; winter, 9:30–4.

VATICAN CITY [*Città del Vaticano*]

• PINACOTECA VATICANA (Vatican Picture Gallery), of the Vatican Museum. Includes one room of contemporary art.

Hours: Closed Sunday; open other days, 9–2.

Spoleto [*Umbria*]

• GALLERIA COMUNALE D'ARTE MODERNA, Palazzo Callicola. Italian paintings of the 20 century bought by the city from the "National Exhibition of Figurative Art" held each year in Spoleto.

Hours: Apply at administrative office.

Trieste [*Venezia*]

• CIVICO MUSEO REVOLTELLA, GALLERIA D'ARTE MODERNA, Via Diaz 27. Works of the late 19 and 20 centuries including Hayez, Bianchi, Mancini, Carrà, Sironi and others.

Hours: Closed Monday; open other days, 10–1.

Turin [*Torino*]

• MUSEO CIVICO, GALLERIA D'ARTE MODERNA, Via Magenta 31, Tel: (011) 41 822. Painting, sculpture and prints of the 19 and 20 centuries including a large collection of 19 century works by Piedmontese artists, also Modigliani, Carrà, Sironi, Morandi, Casorati, Campigli, Martini, Manzù, Marini, Afro, Guttuso, Vedova and others, as well as foreign artists, among whom are Utrillo, Klee, Picasso, Léger, Chagall, Arp, Wols, Hartung, Manessier, Tobey, Tamayo, Chillida.

Hours: Closed Monday; open other days, 10–12:30 and 3–6.

Admission: Sunday, free; other days, 100 lire.

Udine [*Venezia*]

• MUSEO CIVICO E GALLERIE D'ARTE ANTICA E MODERNA (Civic Museum and Galleries of Ancient and Modern Art), in the Castello. Includes a collection of works by 19 century local artists, as well as contemporary works.

Hours: Closed Monday; open Sunday, 9:30–12:30; other days, 10–12 and 2–4.

Venice [*Venezia*]

• "BIENNALE DI VENEZIA," Ca' Giustinian, S. Marco. International exhibition of modern visual arts organized every two years (1964, 1966, etc.) in the Giardini and housed in 26 pavilions belonging to the principal nations of Europe, Asia, Africa and America.

• GALLERIA INTERNAZIONALE D'ARTE MODERNA, Palazzo Pesaro, San Stae. One section of the museum is devoted to Italian art from 1800 to the present, the other to modern foreign works including Corot, Rodin, Klimt, Bonnard, Kandinsky, Nolde, Chagall, Rouault, Dufy, Moore, Tobey and others.

Hours: Closed Monday; open Sunday, 9–12:30; other days, 9:30–12:30 and 3:30–6:30.

• MUSEO VETRARIO (Glass Museum), Palazzo Giustiniano, San Donato, Murano. Includes 19 and 20 century Venetian glass.

Hours: Closed Monday; open Sunday, 9–12:30; other days, 9–12:30 and 2:30–6.

• PEGGY GUGGENHEIM COLLECTION, Palazzo Venier dei Leoni, Dorsoduro 707, San Gregorio. Private collection of 20 century art owned by Miss Peggy Guggenheim; her home, garden and gallery contain works by Picasso, Braque, Léger, Delaunay, Mondrian, van Doesburg, Kandinsky, Klee, Chagall, Brancusi, de Chirico, Ernst, Masson, Magritte, Miró, Tanguy, Dali, Calder,

Cornell, Marini, Moore, Giacometti, Rothko, de Kooning
and Pollock as well as many others.

Hours: August–October, Monday, Wednesday and Friday, 3–5.

Admission: Free.

Verona [*Venezia*]

• GALLERIA D'ARTE MODERNA, Palazzo Forti, Via
Emilei 1. Includes Italian art of 19 and 20 centuries with
works by Ciardi, Fattori, Bianchi, Mafai and others.

Hours: Closed Sunday and Monday; open other days,
9–12 and 2–5.

Publications:

Domus, published monthly in Milan.

La Biennale di Venezia, published quarterly in
Venice.

Civiltà delle Macchine (Civilization of the Ma-
chine Age), published monthly in Rome.

Notiziario d'Arte (Art News), published every
other month in Rome.

Current exhibitions in commercial galleries are
listed in newspapers.

MONACO

Monte-Carlo

• MUSEE NATIONAL DES BEAUX-ARTS, rue des
Genets, Tel: 012 53. Includes works by Vernet and Dufy.

Hours: Closed Monday and month of September; open
other days, 10–12 and 2:30–5.

van Gogh: L'Arlésienne. Rijksmuseum Kröller-Müller

THE NETHERLANDS

Amsterdam

• RIJKSMUSEUM (State Museum), Stadhouder-skade 42, Tel: (020) 73 21 21. Includes works by 19 century artists, among whom are Daumier, Corot, Fantin-Latour, van Gogh, Monticelli.

Hours: Closed January 1; open Sunday, 1–5; other days, 10–5.

Admission: Saturday and Sunday, 25 cents; other days, 50 cents.

• STEDELIJK MUSEUM (Municipal Museum), Paulus Potterstraat 13, Tel: (020) 73 21 66. Dutch and foreign painting and sculpture from 19 century to the present including loan collection of 170 paintings and 300 drawings by van Gogh and works by Cézanne, Renoir, Klee, Chagall, Mondrian, Rietveld, Malevich, Gabo, Arp, Miró, Campigli, Pollock, Dubuffet, Appel, Corneille, Jorn, Alechinsky, among many others; also collections of prints, posters, photographs, films and industrial design; temporary exhibitions.

Hours: Sunday, 1–5; other days, 10–5.
Admission: 25 cents.

Arnhem
• GEMEENTEMUSEUM (Municipal Museum), Utrechtseweg 87, Tel: (08300) 3 18 41. Art of the Province of Gelderland.
Hours: Closed January 1 and April 30; open Sunday, 1–5; other days, 10–5.
Admission: 50 cents.

Eindhoven
• STEDELIJK VAN ABBE MUSEUM (van Abbe Municipal Museum), Bilderdijklaan 10, Tel: (04900) 1 22 80. Primarily 20 century Dutch and Flemish painting, also works by other 20 century European artists including Picasso, Braque, Chagall, Delaunay, Léger, Dufy, Kandinsky, Manessier, Poliakoff, Dubuffet, Tàpies.
Hours: Sunday, 1–5; other days, 10–5 (also, in winter, Tuesday and Thursday evenings, 8–10).
Admission: 20 cents.

The Hague [*'s Gravenhage*]
• GEMEENTEMUSEUM (Municipal Museum), Stadhouderslaan 41, Tel: (070) 51 41 81. Collection of modern painting, sculpture and prints includes large group of early works by Mondrian, as well as work by other *de Stijl* artists.
Hours: Closed January 1; open Sunday, 11–5; other days, 10–5, also Wednesday evening, 8–10.
Admission: 20 cents.

Laren N. H. [*Noord Holland*]

• STICHTING SINGER MEMORIAL FOUNDATION, Oude Drift 1, Tel: (2953) 56 56. Collection of paintings by William Henry Singer, Jr. (1868–1943) and his American and Dutch contemporaries, as well as other paintings, sculpture and prints of the 19 and 20 centuries; also temporary exhibitions.

Hours: Sunday and holidays, 1–5; other days: April–September, 10–5; October–March, 10–4.

Admission: 1 guilder.

Leyden [*Leiden*]

• STEDELIJK MUSEUM DE LAKENHAL (De Lakenhal Municipal Museum), Oude Singel 28-32. Collection includes Dutch painting of the 19 and 20 centuries.

Hours: April–October: Sunday and public holidays, 1–5; other days, 10–5; October–April: Sunday and public holidays, 1–5; other days, 10–4 (except October 3, 10–12).

Admission: Sunday and public holidays, free; other days, 25 cents.

Otterlo

• RIJKSMUSEUM KROLLER-MULLER (Kröller-Müller State Museum), De Hoge Veluwe National Park, Tel: (08383) 2 13. Formerly the private collection of Mrs. H. Kröller-Müller, it includes an extensive section of 19 and 20 century painting, sculpture, prints and drawings with, among many others, works by Redon, Fantin-Latour, Seurat, Signac, Ensor, Picasso, Gris, Severini, Mondrian, Marini, Hepworth and over 270 works by van Gogh. Sculpture Park (reached only through the museum) includes works by Rodin, Bourdelle, Maillol, Epstein, Lipchitz, Arp, Moore, Paolozzi, Chadwick, Wotruba.

Hours: Museum: Sunday and holidays, 1–5:30; other days, 10–5:30. Sculpture Park: April–November: Sunday and holidays, 1–4; other days, 11–4.

Admission: Saturday, 10 cents; other days, 25 cents.

Rotterdam

• MUSEUM BOYMANS-VAN BEUNINGEN, Mathenes-
serlaan 18-20, Tel: (010) 11 74 30. Includes, among
others, paintings by Daumier, Monet, Pissarro, Sisley,
Gauguin, van Gogh, Ensor, Munch, Kandinsky, Kokoschka and sculpture by Rodin, Degas, Renoir, Maillol,
Despiau, Marini, as well as modern prints and drawings.
Hours: Closed Monday; open Sunday, 11–5; other days,
10–5.
Admission: 10 cents.

Utrecht

• FENTENER VAN VLISSINGENHUIS (Centraal
Museum department of modern art), Maliebaan 42, Tel:
(030) 2 58 54. About 370 paintings and prints, mostly
by Dutch artists, from 1850 to the present including van
Gogh, Toorop, Sluyters, van der Leck, Appel, also sculp-
ture, Art Nouveau and modern furniture, glass and
ceramics.
Hours: Sunday, 1–5; other days, 10–5.
Admission: Sunday and Saturday after 1, 10 cents;
Saturday, 10–1 and other days, 20 cents.

• MUSEUM VAN NIEUWE RELIGIEUZE KUNST (Museum of Contemporary Religious Art), (of Aartsbisschop-
pelijk Museum), Lange Nieuwstraat 38, Tel: (030)
2 31 26. Painting, sculpture, prints, stained glass and
needlework from 1870 to the present including works by
Toorop, Kogan, van Rees, Zadkine, Bissière, Manessier,
Joep Nicolas and others.
Hours: Sunday, 2–5; other days, 10–5.

Publications:

Museumjournaal, magazine of modern art in
Dutch museums, published ten times a year by the Stich-
ting Kunstpublicaties, Rijksmuseum Kröller-Müller,
Otterlo.

Munch: Girls on the Bridge. Nasjonalgalleriet, Oslo

NORWAY

Bergen

• BERGENS BILLEDGALLERI (Bergen Picture Gallery), Tel: 1 78 39. Collection of Norwegian painting.

Hours: Closed Monday; open May 23–August 31: Sunday, 12–3; other days, 10–3; September 1–May 22: Tuesday–Sunday, 12–3.

Admission: 1 krone.

• RASMUS MEYERS SAMLINGER (Rasmus Meyer Collection), (of the Bergen Municipal Art Museums), Lars Hillesgate 8, Tel: 1 78 39. Norwegian art of the 19 and 20 centuries forms the core of the painting collection including 32 paintings and 105 prints and drawings by Munch, also works by Krohg, Sørenson, Astrup, among others.

Hours: May 23–August 31: Sunday, 12–3; other days,
10–3; September 1–May 22: Tuesday only, 12–3.
Admission: 1 krone.

• VESTLANDSKE KUNSTINDUSTRIMUSEUM (West-
ern Norway Museum of Applied Arts), Tel: 1 51 08.
Hours: May 23–August 31: Sunday, 12–3; other days,
10–3; September 1–May 22: Sunday and
Wednesday only, 12–2.
Admission: 1 krone.

Oslo
• KUNSTINDUSTRIMUSEET (Museum of Applied
Arts), St. Olavsgate 1. Includes collections of contemporary Norwegian and foreign ceramics, glass, furniture,
textiles, metalwork.
Hours: Closed Monday; open Sunday, 12–3; other days,
11–3.
Admission: Sunday, free; other days: adults, 2 kroner;
children, 0.50 krone.

• KUNSTNERNES HUS (Artists' Center), Werge-
landsveien 17–19. Norwegian and foreign arts and crafts;
also temporary loan exhibitions of modern art.
Hours: Sunday, 12–4; Wednesday, 10–8; other days,
10–4.
Admission: Adults, 2 kroner; children, 1 krone.

• MUNCH-MUSEET, Töyengaten 53. Museum is
due to be opened in June 1963 and will be devoted to the
work of Edvard Munch (1863–1944).

• NASJONALGALLERIET (National Gallery), Uni-
versitetsgaten 13, Tel: 33 02 76. Contains Norway's most
important collection of 19 and 20 century foreign and
Norwegian painting and sculpture including works by
Courbet, Manet, Renoir, Cézanne, Gauguin, Munch, Bonnard, Matisse, Picasso, Léger, Rouault, Modigliani, Manes-

sier, Tamayo, Bazaine; also temporary exhibitions including modern art.

Hours: Sunday, 12–3; other days, 11–3, also Wednesday evening, 6–8.

Admission: Free.

• VIGELANDMUSEET, Nobelsgate 32. Contains sculpture and approximately 800 studies and hundreds of woodcuts by Gustav Vigeland (1869–1943); also large group of his sculpture in adjoining Frogner Municipal Park.

Hours: Closed Monday; open other days, 1–7.

Admission: Free.

Trondheim [*Trondhjem*]

• NORDENFJELDSKE KUNSTINDUSTRIMUSEUM (Northern Norway Museum of Applied Arts), Dronningensgate 1b. Includes furniture, textiles, glass, ceramics and metalwork of the present.

Hours: May 15–September 1: Sunday, 12–3; other days, 10–3; September 2–May 14: daily, 12–3.

Admission: Adults, 1 krone; children, 0.50 krone.

• TRONDHJEMS FASTE GALLERI (Trondheim Permanent Exhibition Gallery).

Hours: Closed Monday; open other days, 12–3.

Admission: Adults, 1 krone; children, 0.50 krone.

Publications:

Kunsten Idag (Art of Today), published quarterly by Per Rom, Radhusgaten 19, Oslo.

Kunst og Kultur (Art and Culture), published quarterly by Gyldendal Norsk Forlag, Oslo.

Bonytt (Design for Living), applied arts magazine, published ten times a year by the National Society of Norwegian Arts, Crafts and Industrial Design, Oscarsgaten 42, Oslo.

Corner of Neoplastic Hall, Muzeum Sztuki, Lódz

POLAND

Interior, Muzeum Sztuki, Lódz

Cracow [Kraków]

• MUZEUM NARODOWE (National Museum), ul. Manifestu Lipcowego 10–12. Includes 19 and 20 century Polish art.

Lódz

• MUZEUM SZTUKI W LODZI (Lódz Art Museum), ul. Wieckowskiego 36, Tel: 382 73. Includes Polish and foreign art of 19 and 20 centuries with works by the Polish artists Katarzyna Kobro, Henryk Stazewski, Józef Pankiewicz, Wladyslaw Strzeminski, Jerzy Tchórzewski, among others, and works by Renoir, Signac, van Doesburg, Jawlensky, Klee, Arp, Ernst, Schwitters, Léger, Ozenfant, Baumeister, Matta, Lurçat, Vasarely, Zañartu, Baj and others.

Hours: Closed Monday; open Sunday, 10–5; Tuesday and Thursday, 11–7; other days, 9–3.

Admission: 1 zloty; students, soldiers and groups, reduced rate.

Poznan

• MUZEUM NARODOWE (National Museum), al. Marcinkowskiego 3, Tel: 13 04, 19 69. Collection includes Polish painting and sculpture of 19 and 20 centuries.

Warsaw [Warszawa]

• MUZEUM NARODOWE W WARSZAVIE (Warsaw National Museum), al. Jerozolimskie 3. Includes collection of modern Polish and foreign painting, sculpture, prints, drawings and applied arts.

Publications:

Przeglad Artystyczny (Artists' Review), ul. Dlugaz 6, Warsaw; six issues a year.

PORTUGAL

Aveiro
• MUSEU DE AVEIRO, in Convento de Santa Joana Princesa, Rua de Santa Joana Princesa. Includes art of 20 century with works by Fausto Sampaio, Vasco Branco, Gaspar Albino, Eduardo Zinle and others.

Hours: Closed Monday; open other days, 10–12:30 and 2–5.

Admission: Sunday and Thursday, free; other days, 2.50 escudos.

Bragança
• MUSEU DO ABADE DE BAÇAL (Baçal Abbey Museum), in the Paço Episcopal (Bishop's Residence), Rua Conselheiro Abilio Beça. Includes collection of 20 century Portuguese art.

Hours: Closed Monday; open other days, 10–12:30 and 2–5.

Admission: Sunday and Thursday, free; other days, 2.50 escudos.

Caldas da Raínha
• MUSEU DE JOSE MALHOA, in Parque Dom Carlos I. Includes collections of contemporary painting and sculpture.

Hours: Closed Monday and bank holidays; open other days, 10–5.

Admission: Sunday and Thursday, free; other days, 2.50 escudos.

Coimbra
• MUSEU MACHADO DE CASTRO, Largo Dr. José Rodrigues. Includes sculpture, painting and applied arts of 19 century.

Hours: Closed Monday; open other days, 10–5.

Admission: Sunday and Thursday, free; other days, 2.50 escudos.

Evora
• MUSEU REGIONAL, in the Igreja das Mercês (Church of the Graces), Largo do Conde de Vila Flor. Includes collection of 20 century Portuguese art.

Hours: Closed Monday; open other days, 10–12:30 and 2–5.

Admission: Sunday and Thursday, free; other days, 2.50 escudos.

Lisbon [*Lisboa*]
• MUSEU NACIONAL DE ARTE CONTEMPORANEA, in a portion of Convento de São Francisco, Rua de Serpa Pinto 6. Art of late 19 and 20 centuries.

Hours: Closed Monday; open other days, 10–12:30 and 2–5.

Admission: Sunday and Thursday, free; other days, 2.50 escudos.

Oporto [*Pôrto*]
• MUSEU NACIONAL DE SOARES DOS REIS, Palacio dos Carrancas, Rua Dom Manuel II. Includes a room of modern art.

Hours: Closed Monday; open other days, 10–5.

Admission: Sunday and Thursday, free; other days, 2.50 escudos.

Publications:
Colóquio: Revista de Artes e Letras, published five times a year by Fundação Calouste Gulbenkian, Avenida de Berna, Parque de Santa Gertrudes, Lisbon.

Art Museum of the Romanian People's Republic, Bucharest

ROMANIA

Arad
• ARAD MUSEUM, Piata Xenopol 1. Includes modern Romanian and foreign art.
Hours: Closed Monday; open other days, 10–7.
Admission: 1 leu; students, soldiers, artists, 0.50 lei.

Bacau
• BACAU MUSEUM, Strada Marasesti 43. Includes modern Romanian art.
Hours: Closed Monday; open other days, 10–7.
Admission: 1 leu; students, soldiers, artists, 0.50 lei.

Baia Mare

• BAIA MARE MUSEUM, Strada 1 Mai 8. Includes collections of modern Romanian and Hungarian art.
Hours: Closed Monday; open other days, 10–7.
Admission: 1 leu; students, soldiers, artists, 0.50 lei.

Botosani

• BOTOSANI MUSEUM, Calea Nationala 20. Includes modern Romanian art.
Hours: Closed Monday; open other days, 10–7.
Admission: 1 leu; students, soldiers, artists, 0.50 lei.

Braila

• BRAILA ART MUSEUM, Piata Lenin 1. Contains modern Romanian art.
Hours: Closed Monday; open other days, 10–7.
Admission: 1 leu; students, soldiers, artists, 0.50 lei.

Brasov

• BRASOV MUSEUM, Piata 23 August 30. Includes modern Romanian art of the Brasov region.
Hours: Closed Monday; open other days, 10–7.
Admission: 1 leu; students, soldiers, artists, 0.50 lei.

Bucharest [*Bucuresti*]

• ACADEMY OF THE ROMANIAN PEOPLE'S REPUBLIC, PRINT DEPARTMENT, Calea Victoriei 125. Contains extensive collection of drawings, prints and Romanian and foreign watercolors.
Hours: Closed Monday; open other days, 10–7.

• ART MUSEUM OF THE ROMANIAN PEOPLE'S REPUBLIC, Calea Victoriei 11, Tel: 13 06 60. Contains country's most important collection of Romanian art of 19 and 20 centuries, also foreign painting, sculpture, prints and drawings of 19 and 20 centuries including works by

Daumier, Rodin, Brancusi, among others.

Hours: Closed Monday; open other days, 10–7.

Admission: 1 leu; students, soldiers, artists, 0.50 lei.

• CORNEL MEDREA MUSEUM, Strada General Budisteanu 16. Contains collection of works by Romanian sculptor Medrea (born 1888).

Hours: Closed Monday; open other days, 10–7.

Admission: 1 leu; students, soldiers, artists, 0.50 lei.

• ELENA DONA AND DR. IOSIF N. DONA COLLECTION, Strada Dr. Dona 12. Formerly the Dona private collection, it includes modern Romanian art.

Hours: Closed Monday; open other days, 10–7.

Admission: 1 leu; students, soldiers, artists, 0.50 lei.

• FREDERIC STORCK AND CECILIA CULTESCU-STORCK ART MUSEUM, Strada Vasile Alecsandri 16. Sculpture, drawings and other works by the Storck family of sculptors housed in their studio, also their personal collections.

Hours: Closed Monday; open other days, 10–7.

Admission: 1 leu; students, soldiers, artists, 0.50 lei.

• GHEORGHE TATTARESCU MEMORIAL MUSEUM, Strada Dobrogeanu Gherea 7. Home and studio of the painter Tattarescu (1820–1894) contains collection of his paintings and drawings.

Hours: Closed Monday; open other days, 10–7.

Admission: 1 leu; students, soldiers, artists, 0.50 lei.

• MISU M. WEIMBERG COLLECTION, Strada Alex. Sahia 16. Contains representative works by contemporary Romanian painters including paintings, drawings and prints by Iosif Iser (1881–1958).

Hours: Closed Monday; open other days, 10–7.

Admission: 1 leu; students, soldiers, artists, 0.50 lei.

• THEODOR AMAN MUSEUM, Strada C. A. Rosetti
8. Home and studio of the painter Aman (1831–1891)
contains extensive collection of his paintings and drawings.
Hours: Closed Monday; open other days, 10–7.
Admission: 1 leu; students, soldiers, artists, 0.50 lei.

• ZAMBACCIAN MUSEUM, Strada Muzeul Zambaccian 21. Extensive collection of Romanian and French
modern art given to the State by the collector Zambaccian.
Hours: Closed Monday; open other days, 10–7.
Admission: 1 leu; students, soldiers, artists, 0.50 lei.

Caracal
• CARACAL MUSEUM, Strada Negru Voda 1. In-
cludes modern Romanian art.
Hours: Closed Monday; open other days, 10–7.
Admission: 1 leu; students, soldiers, artists, 0.50 lei.

Cimpina
• NICOLAE GRIGORESCU MEMORIAL MUSEUM. Col-
lection of works by the Romanian painter Grigorescu
(1838–1907), also personal souvenirs.
Hours: Closed Monday; open other days, 10–7.
Admission: 1 leu; students, soldiers, artists, 0.50 lei.

Cimpulung
• CIMPULUNG-MUSCEL MUSEUM, Republicii 3.
Includes modern Romanian art.
Hours: Closed Monday; open other days, 10–7.
Admission: 1 leu; students, soldiers, artists, 0.50 lei.

Cluj
• CLUJ ART MUSEUM, Piata Libertatii 30. In-
cludes modern Romanian art.
Hours: Closed Monday; open other days, 10–7.
Admission: 1 leu; students, soldiers, artists, 0.50 lei.

Constantza
• CONSTANTZA ART MUSEUM, Strada Elena Pavel

12. Contains extensive collection of Romanian modern art.

Hours: Closed Monday; open other days, 10–7.

Admission: 1 leu; students, soldiers, artists, 0.50 lei.

Craiova
• CRAIOVA ART MUSEUM, Calea Lenin 17. Includes Romanian modern art.

Hours: Closed Monday; open other days, 10–7.

Admission: 1 leu; students, soldiers, artists, 0.50 lei.

Galatzi
• GALATZI ART MUSEUM, Calea Republicii 104. Contains modern Romanian art.

Hours: Closed Monday; open other days, 10–7.

Admission: 1 leu; students, soldiers, artists, 0.50 lei.

Iasi
• IASI ART MUSEUM, Strada Malinovski 1. Contains modern Romanian art.

Hours: Closed Monday; open other days, 10–7.

Admission: 1 leu; students, soldiers, artists, 0.50 lei.

Piatra-Neamt
• PIATRA-NEAMT MUSEUM, Piata Stefan cel Mare. Includes modern Romanian art.

Hours: Closed Monday; open other days, 10–7.

Admission: 1 leu; students, soldiers, artists, 0.50 lei.

Ploiesti
• PLOIESTI ART MUSEUM, Strada Krupskaia 1. Contains Romanian modern art.

Hours: Closed Monday; open other days, 10–7.

Admission: 1 leu; students, soldiers, artists, 0.50 lei.

Rimnicul Sarat
• RIMNICUL SARAT MUSEUM. Contains modern Romanian painting, sculpture and prints.

Hours: Closed Monday; open other days, 10–7.
Admission: 1 leu; students, soldiers, artists, 0.50 lei.

Roman
• ROMAN MUSEUM, Strada Stefan cel Mare. Includes modern Romanian art.
Hours: Closed Monday; open other days, 10–7.
Admission: 1 leu; students, soldiers, artists, 0.50 lei.

Sf. Gheorghe
• SF. GHEORGHE MUSEUM. Includes modern Romanian art.
Hours: Closed Monday; open other days, 10–7.
Admission: 1 leu; students, soldiers, artists, 0.50 lei.

Sibiu
• BRUCKENTHAL MUSEUM, Piata Republicii 3. Includes contemporary Romanian art.
Hours: Closed Monday; open other days, 10–7.
Admission: 1 leu; students, soldiers, artists, 0.50 lei.

Tirgu Jiu
• TOWN PARK contains sculpture by Constantin Brancusi (1876–1957), who once lived here.

Tirgu Mures
• TIRGU MURES ART MUSEUM, Piata Eroilor Sovietici 1. Contains contemporary Romanian art as well as foreign art of the 19 and 20 centuries.
Hours: Closed Monday; open other days, 10–7.
Admission: 1 leu; students, soldiers, artists, 0.50 lei.

Publications:
Viata Culturala a Capitalei (The Cultural Life in Our Capital), Bucharest, lists current exhibitions in modern art galleries.

RUSSIA [*see U.S.S.R.*]

Whistler: Portrait of Thomas Carlyle.
Glasgow Art Gallery and Museum

SCOTLAND

Aberdeen
• ABERDEEN ART GALLERY, School Hill, Tel:
23456. Contains the Macdonald Collection including works
by Sargent, Sickert, John, Laurencin, Epstein, Léger,

Nicholson and the Kynett Collection of etchings by James McBey (1883-1959).
Hours: Sunday, 2–5; other days, 10–5.
Admission: Free.

Dundee [*Angus*]
• DUNDEE CENTRAL MUSEUM AND VICTORIA ART GALLERIES, Albert Square, Tel: 25492. Includes British art of the present with emphasis on Scottish artists.
Hours: Monday–Saturday, 10–6 (winter, 10–5).
Admission: Free.

• ORCHAR ART GALLERY, Broughty Ferry, Tel: 77337. Includes 36 etchings by James McNeill Whistler (1834–1903).
Hours: June–September: Sunday, 3–5 and 6–7:30; Thursday, 10–1; other days, 10–1, 3–5 and 6–7:30; October–May: Sunday, 2–4; Thursday, 11–1; other days, 11–1 and 2–4.
Admission: Free.

Edinburgh
• NATIONAL GALLERY OF SCOTLAND, The Mound, Tel: CAL 6824. Includes collections of 19 and 20 century Scottish and foreign painting, sculpture, drawings and prints with works by Monet, Pissarro, Degas, Gauguin, van Gogh, Fantin-Latour, Rodin, Monticelli, Klee and others.
Hours: Sunday, 2–5 (2–4, December and January); other days, 10–5 (10–8 during Edinburgh International Festival).
Admission: Free.

• SCOTTISH NATIONAL GALLERY OF MODERN ART, Royal Botanic Gardens, Tel: DEA 3754. Opened in 1960, the Gallery and its adjoining garden contain 20 century painting, sculpture, drawings and prints.
Hours: Sunday, 2–5 (or until 10 minutes before garden

closes if this is earlier); other days, 11–6 (or until 10 minutes before garden closes if this is earlier).

Admission: Free.

Glasgow

• CITY OF GLASGOW CORPORATION ART GALLERY AND MUSEUM, Kelvingrove, Tel: KEL 1134. Includes British and foreign painting of 19 and 20 centuries; contains the McInnes Collection of modern French painting with works by Monet, Seurat, Cézanne, van Gogh, Matisse and Braque, also the Burrell Collection (eventually to be separately housed) with emphasis on 19 century French art including works by Manet, Sisley and 23 paintings and drawings by Degas.

Hours: Sunday, 2–5; other days, 10–5.
Admission: Free.

• THE HUNTERIAN MUSEUM, Glasgow University, Tel: KEL 2231. University art collection includes works by Whistler, among others.

Hours: Closed Sunday; open Saturday, 10–12; other days, 10–5.
Admission: Free.

Kirkcaldy [*Fife*]

• KIRKCALDY MUSEUM AND ART GALLERY, War Memorial Grounds, Tel: 2732. Art Gallery contains mainly Scottish art of 19 and 20 centuries with rooms devoted to William McTaggart (1835–1910) and S. J. Peploe (1871–1935), also includes works by Corot, Boudin, Sickert, Fantin-Latour, Gillies.

Hours: Sunday, 2–5; other days, 1:30–5.
Admission: Free.

Publications:

Scottish Art Review, published twice a year by Glasgow Art Gallery and Museums Association, Kelvingrove, Glasgow.

SPAIN

Barcelona

• AMIGOS DE GAUDI, Palacio Güell, Conde del Asalto 3-5. Archives of drawings, photographs, documents pertaining to the work of the Catalan architect Antoni Gaudí (1852–1926); house and decorations were designed by him as was Parque Güell in this city.
Hours: Closed Monday; open other days, 10–2 and 6–8.
Admission: 6 pesetas.

• MUSEO DE ARTE CONTEMPORANEO, Antiguo Hospital de la Santa Cruz, Carmen 47. Collection of modern Spanish and foreign painting.
Hours: Sunday, 12–2; other days, 12–2 and 6–9.

• MUSEO DE ARTE MODERNO, Palacio de la Ciudadela, Parque de la Ciudadela, Tel: 222 42 77. Spanish (in particular Catalan) and foreign painting, sculpture and drawings of 19 and 20 centuries with works by Fortuny, Rusiñol, Casas, Sorolla, Zuloaga, Picasso, among others.
Hours: Daily, 10–2.
Admission: 5 pesetas.

• MUSEO PICASSO, Calle de Moncada 15. To be opened, museum will contain paintings, prints, drawings and ceramics by Picasso, as well as his ceramic murals on exterior of building.

Bilbao [*Vizcaya*]
• MUSEO DE BELLAS ARTES Y DE ARTE MODERNO, Parque de Tres Naciones. Contains, among others, works by Sorolla, Zuloaga, Madrazo, Zubiaurre, Solana, Gauguin, Campigli.
Hours: Daily, morning and afternoon.
Admission: 1.20 pesetas.

Cadiz
• MUSEO DE BELLAS ARTES, Plaza de Mina. Includes room of 19 century art.
Hours: Daily, 10:30–1:30 and 3:30–5:30.
Admission: Sunday and holidays, 11–1, free; other times, 5 pesetas.

Córdoba
• MUSEO JULIO ROMERO DE TORRES, in Museo Provincial de Bellas Artes, Plaza del Potro. Devoted to the artist Romero de Torres (1880–1930).
Hours: Daily, morning and afternoon.
Admission: Free.

Lérida
• MUSEO DE ARTE MODERNO JAIME MORERA, Antiguo Hospital de Santa Maria, Avenida de Blondel.

Modern paintings, including a collection of works by
Morera (1854–1927), also some works by Haes and
Fortuny.

Madrid

• MUSEO CERRALBO, Calle de Ventura Rodriguez
17. Former private collection of the Marquis of Cerralbo,
includes works by some modern Spanish painters.
Hours: Closed Tuesday; open other days, 9:30–1:30.
Admission: 3 pesetas.

• MUSEO DE ARTE CONTEMPORANEO, Biblioteca
Nacional, Paseo de Calvo Sotelo 20, Tel: 275 96 28. Con-
tains more than 300 works: paintings, drawings, sculpture,
by Spanish artists born after 1880 including Picasso,
Maria Blanchard, Solana, Gris, Dali, Tàpies, Chillida and
others.
Hours: Daily, 10–2.
Admission: 5 pesetas.

• MUSEO DE ARTE DEL SIGLO XIX (Museum of
Art of the 19 Century), Paseo de Calvo Sotelo 20. Former-
ly the Museo de Arte Moderno, it contains painting of the
19 century (1801–1885), predominantly Spanish.
Hours: Daily, morning and afternoon.
Admission: 2 pesetas.

• MUSEO DE LA REAL ACADEMIA DE BELLAS ARTES
DE SAN FERNANDO, Calle de Alcalá 13, Tel: 232 04 24.
Contains works by Sorolla, Hermoso, Blay, Clará, Zubi-
aurre and others.
Hours: Daily, 10–1:30 and 4–6.
Admission: Sunday and holidays, 5 pesetas; other days,
7 pesetas.

• MUSEO JOAQUIN SOROLLA, Calle del General
Martínez Campos 33. Permanent exhibition of 350 works
by Sorolla (1863–1923) including paintings, sculpture,

drawings and ceramics, as well as his personal collection; one room devoted to studies for large paintings by him in the museum of the Hispanic Society, New York.
Hours: Closed Monday; open other days, 10–2.
Admission: 5 pesetas.

• MUSEO ZULOAGA, Plaza de Gabriel Miró. Paintings and drawings by Ignacio Zuloaga (1870–1945).
Hours: Closed Tuesday; open other days, 10–2.
Admission: Free.

• SALAS DE EXPOSICIONES DEL ATENEO DE MADRID, Tel: 221 43 39. Temporary loan exhibitions.
Hours: Daily, 5–9.
Admission: Free.

Málaga
• MUSEO PROVINCIAL DE BELLAS ARTES, Calle de San Agustín. Contains several galleries of works by, among others, Mélida, Sorolla, Rosales and two early Picasso paintings.
Hours: Daily: summer, 10–1:30 and 5–8; winter, 10–1:30 and 4–7.
Admission: 10 pesetas.

Olot [*Gerona*]
• MUSEO DE ARTE MODERNO, Parque de la Ciudad. Contains, among others, works by Llimona, Casas, Blay, Nonell, Clará.
Hours: Daily, morning and afternoon.
Admission: 1 peseta.

Palamós [*Gerona*]
• MUSEO CAU DE LA COSTA BRAVA, Plaza del Horno 4. Primarily prehistoric objects, but also includes collection of modern paintings by J. M. Sert, Vila-Puig and Mascort.
Hours: Holidays, 11–1 and 5–8; other days, 6–8.
Admission: 5 pesetas.

Pontevedra
• Museo de Pontevedra, Plaza de la Leña. Includes works of the 19 century by Rusiñol, Becquer, Villamil, among others.
Hours: Daily, morning and afternoon.
Admission: Free.

Reus [*Tarragona*]
• Museo Municipal Prim Rull, Calle de San Juan 27. Contains drawings and paintings by Fortuny and Gaudí.
Hours: Closed Wednesday.
Admission: 5 pesetas.

San Sebastián [*Guipúzcoa*]
• Museo Municipal de San Telmo, Convento San Telmo. Housed in former abbey, museum contains paintings by Zuloaga, Ortiz, Zubiaurre and others; murals in chapel by José María Sert.
Hours: Daily: summer, 10–1:30 and 4–8; winter, 10–1:30 and 3–6.
Admission: 5 pesetas.

Seville
• Museo Provincial de Bellas Artes, Convento de la Merced, Plaza del Museo 8. Contains several rooms devoted to modern art.
Hours: Holidays, 11–2; other days, 10–2.
Admission: 5 pesetas.

Sitges [*near Barcelona*]
• Museo del Cau Ferrat, Calle de Fenollar. Former home of the artist-writer Santiago Rusiñol (1861–1931), contains works by him as well as by Casas, Zuloaga, Picasso and others.
Hours: Closed Monday; open other days, 10–1:30 and 4–7.
Admission: 5 pesetas, which includes admission to Museo Maricel.

• Museo Maricel, Calle de Fenollar. Contains two rooms of modern paintings by Rusiñol, Roig, Soler, Sunyer, among others.

Hours: Closed Monday; open other days, 10–1:30 and 4–7.

Tossa de Mar [*Gerona*]
• Museo Municipal. Primarily modern art, including works by Chagall.

Hours: Summer, daily; winter, by appointment only.

Admission: 5 pesetas.

Valencia
• Museo Provincial de Bellas Artes, Calle de San Pio V 9. Contains one floor devoted to Valencian modern art and one room of works by Sorolla.

Hours: Daily, 10–2.

Admission: Sunday, free; other days, 2 pesetas.

Villanueva y Geltrú [*near Barcelona*]
• Museo Balaguer, Plaza de la Estación. Includes works by Anglada, Sorolla, Fortuny, Rusiñol, Casas and others.

Hours: Closed Monday; open other days, 4–6 (winter, 3–5).

Admission: Free.

Vitoria [*Alava*]
• Museo de Arte Moderno, Calle de Cercas Bajas y Samaniego. Contains works by modern artists from the Province of Alava.

Hours: Daily, mornings.

Admission: Free.

Zaragoza [*Aragón*]

• MUSEO PROVINCIAL DE BELLAS ARTES, Plaza de José Antonio 6. Includes works by, among others, Haes, Sorolla, Rusiñol, Zuloaga and contemporary Aragonese artists.

Hours: Sunday and holidays, 10–1; other days, 9–3.
Admission: 5 pesetas.

Zumaya [*Guipúzcoa*]

• CASA MUSEO IGNACIO ZULOAGA. Former home of Zuloaga (1870–1945), contains primarily his works.

Publications:

Goya, Serrano 122, Madrid.

Göteborgs Konstmuseum, Göteborg

SWEDEN

Interior, Moderna Museet, Stockholm

NOTE: *Swedish museums usually charge no admission or only a nominal fee.*

Eskilstuna
• ESKILSTUNA KONSTMUSEUM, Kyrkogatan. Painting, sculpture, drawings and photographs, mainly Scandinavian.
Hours: Daily, 1–4; also Tuesday and Thursday evenings, 7–9.

Göteborg
• GOTEBORGS KONSTMUSEUM, Götaplatsen, Tel: 18 95 37. Includes French painting from impressionism to the present, also an extensive collection of modern Scandinavian painting and sculpture.
Hours: Sunday, 12–4; other days, 10–4.

• ROHSSKA KONSTSLOJDMUSEET (Röhss Museum of Arts and Crafts), 37-39 Vasagatan, Tel: 18 22 28. Includes a department devoted to 20 century crafts, mostly the work of Scandinavian designers.
Hours: Sunday, 12–4; others days, 11–3.

Lidingö [*near Stockholm*]
• MILLESGARDEN. Home of Swedish sculptor Carl Milles (1875-1955); house and garden were designed by him and contain vast collection of his sculpture, also works by other artists including impressionists.
Hours: May–October, Tuesday–Sunday, 12–5; June and July, also Tuesday and Friday evenings, 7–9.

Lund
• ARKIV FOR DEKORATIV KONST (Archives of Decorative Art), Finngatan 2, Tel: 1 27 50. Includes preparatory material used in the creation of monumental works: preliminary sketches and study material, full-scale models, original designs.
Hours: Daily, 1–4.

Malmö
• MALMO MUSEUM, Malmöhusvägen, Tel: 7 33 30. Includes fine and applied arts of 19 and 20 centuries, mainly Scandinavian; also, occasionally, temporary exhibitions of modern art.
Hours: Sunday, 11–4; other days, 12–4, also Thursday evening, 6–8.

Mora
• ZORNMUSEET. Primarily works by the Swedish painter and graphic artist Anders Zorn (1860–1920).
Hours: June–August: Sunday, 1–6; other days, 11–6; September–May: Sunday, 1–5; other days, 12–5.

Norrköping
• NORRKOPINGS MUSEUM. Art collections contain exclusively Swedish works with emphasis on 19 and 20 centuries.
Hours: Daily, 1–4, Tuesday and Friday evenings, 7–9.

Orebro
• OREBRO LANS MUSEUM. Includes gallery devoted to modern art; also temporary loan exhibitions of modern art.
Hours: May 15–September 15: Sunday, 1–5; other days, 11–4.

Stockholm
• MODERNA MUSEET, Skeppsholmen. Swedish and foreign painting and sculpture executed after 1910,

including works by Munch, Despiau, Picasso, Matisse, Kandinsky, Calder.

Hours: Sunday, 1–4; Tuesday–Saturday, 12–5.

• NATIONALMUSEUM, Södra Blasieholmshamnen, Tel: 10 51 02. Scandinavian art forms the main part of the 19 and 20 century collection which includes also works by Manet, Renoir, Bonnard, Despiau, Chagall, Derain, Matisse, Léger, Braque, Picasso and others, also collections of contemporary drawings, prints and crafts.

Hours: Sunday, 1–4; Tuesday–Saturday, 10–4.

• THIELSKA GALLERIET (Thiel Gallery), Djurgarden, Tel: 62 34 05. Collection devoted mainly to Swedish art of 1890–1905, with some works from Norway, Denmark and France.

Hours: Sunday, 1–4; other days, 11–3.

• WALDEMARSUDDE (Residence of Prince Eugen), Djurgarden, Tel: 62 18 32. One of the largest painting collections in Sweden, it consists mainly of works by Prince Eugen (1865–1947) and other Swedish artists.

Hours: Sunday, 11–5; June 15–August 31, Tuesday–Saturday, 11–5, also Wednesday and Friday evenings, 7–9; September 1–June 14, Tuesday–Saturday, 11–4.

Publications:

Konstrevy (Art Review), published five times a year, Box 3159, Kammakargatan 9A, Stockholm.

Paletten, published quarterly, Dr. Westringsgata 19A, Göteborg.

Form, applied arts magazine, published ten times a year by Swedish Society for Industrial Design, Svenska Slöjdföreningen, Box 7047, Stockholm.

Stockholm daily newspapers, *Dagens Nyheter* and *Svenska Dagbladet,* list current exhibitions in commercial galleries of modern art.

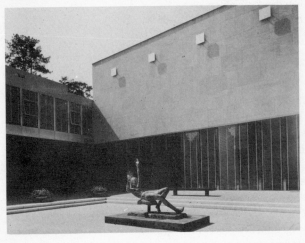

Probst sculpture, Kunsthaus, Aarau

SWITZERLAND

Kunstmuseum, Lucerne

Aarau

• KUNSTHAUS, Rathausplatz, Tel: (064) 2 18 51.
Contains large collection of works by Swiss artists of the
19 and 20 centuries including Stäbli, Amiet, Auberjonois
and others; also temporary exhibitions.

Hours: Closed Monday; open other days, 10–12 and
2–5.

Admission: Free.

Basel

• GEWERBEMUSEUM (Crafts Museum), Spalen-
vorstadt 2, Tel: (061) 23 38 58. Includes collections of
modern furniture, textiles, ceramics, glass, graphic arts;
also temporary exhibitions of modern applied arts.

Hours: During exhibitions, daily, 10–12 and 2–5, also
Wednesday evening, 8–10.

Admission: Free.

• KUNSTHALLE, Steinenberg 7, Tel: (061)
24 48 77. Regular temporary exhibitions of modern art.

Hours: Daily, 10–12:15 and 2–5, also Tuesday and Thursday evenings, 8–10.

Admission: Wednesday and Sunday afternoons, 1.60
Swiss francs; other times, 2 Swiss francs.

• KUNSTMUSEUM, OFFENTLICHE KUNSTSAMM-
LUNG (Art Museum, Public Art Collection), St. Albangra-
ben 16, Tel: (061) 23 18 54. Includes 19 and 20 century
painting, sculpture and prints with, among many others,
works by Cézanne, Rodin, Gauguin, van Gogh, Matisse,
Rouault, Kandinsky, Marc, Klee, Mondrian, Pevsner, de
Chirico, Chagall, Arp, Ernst, Miró, Morandi, Moore,
Calder, Rothko, Francis and an extensive group of cubist
works.

Hours: Sunday, 10:15–12:15 and 2–5; other days, 9–
12:30 (winter, 10–12:30) and 2–5, also Wednesday evening, 8–10.

Admission: Wednesday afternoon and evening and Sunday, free; other times, 1 Swiss franc.

Bern

• KUNSTHALLE BERN, Helvetiaplatz 1, Tel:
(031) 2 24 15. Organizes regular temporary exhibitions
of contemporary painting, sculpture and graphic arts.
Hours: Daily, 10–12 and 2–5, also Thursday evening,
8–10.

• KUNSTMUSEUM, Ferdinand Hodlerstrasse 12,
Tel: (031) 2 09 44. Contains collections of works by 19
and 20 century Swiss and other European artists including Manet, Hodler, Cézanne, Bonnard, Matisse, Chagall,
Jawlensky, Miró; also houses the Paul Klee Foundation
with approximately 40 paintings, 200 sketches, over 2000
drawings and an almost complete collection of prints by
Klee (1879–1940).
Hours: Daily, 10–12 and 2–5.
Admission: Sunday afternoon, free; other times, 1 Swiss
franc.

Chur

• KUNSTHAUS, Villa Planta, Grabenstrasse. Contains the Grisons Art Collection of works of the late 19
century and the 20 century by Swiss and foreign artists
including Segantini, Augusto Giacometti, Kirchner, Al-
berto Giacometti and others; also temporary exhibitions.
Hours: Closed Monday; open Sunday, 10–12 and 2–4;
other days, 9–12 and 2–5.
Admission: Sunday, free; other days, 1 Swiss franc.

Fribourg

• MUSEE D'ART ET D'HISTOIRE, 227 rue Pierre
Aeby, Tel: (037) 2 14 66. Includes works by Swiss artists
of the 19 and 20 centuries, as well as paintings by Courbet,
Fortuny and others in the Marcello Collection.
Hours: Closed Monday; open other days, 10–12 and 2–5.
Admission: Sunday, free; other days, 1.10 Swiss francs.

Geneva [*Genève*]

• Musée d'Art et d'Histoire, rue Charles Galland, Tel: (022) 25 92 36. Includes collection of works by Ferdinand Hodler (1853–1918), also modern French art with works by Corot, Rodin, Fantin-Latour, the impressionists, van Gogh, Gauguin, Rouault, Dufy and Chagall.

• Musée de l'Athenee (Atheneum Museum), 2 rue de l'Athénée (2d floor), Tel: (022) 25 67 13. Organizes temporary exhibitions of modern art.
Hours: Sunday, 10–12; other days, 10–12 and 2–5.
Admission: 1 or 2 Swiss francs, according to the exhibition.

Glarus

• Kunsthaus, Museumsstrasse, Tel: (058) 5 25 35. Contains modern works by Swiss artists including Hodler, Vallotton, Soldenhoff, Amiet, Auberjonois, Haller, Hubacher, also works by Kirchner; temporary exhibitions including modern art.
Hours: Summer, daily, 10–12 and 2–5; other times, by appointment only.
Admission: 1 Swiss franc.

La Chaux-de-Fonds

• Musée des Beaux-Arts, 33 rue de l'Envers, Tel: (039) 2 13 50. Includes collection of contemporary Swiss and foreign art with works by Zadkine, Le Corbusier, Lurçat, Lagrange, Manessier, Bissière, Pignon, Afro, Santomaso, Singier, Adam; also temporary exhibitions of contemporary Swiss and foreign art.
Hours: Closed Monday; open other days, 10–12 and 2–5.
Admission: Free.

Lausanne

• Musée Cantonal des Beaux-Arts, Palais de Rumine, place de la Riponne. Collection includes paint-

ing, sculpture, prints and drawings by 19 and 20 century
Swiss and foreign artists, among whom are Hodler, Val-
lotton, Gleyre, Auberjonois and Corot, Courbet, Cézanne,
Degas, Rodin, Renoir, Maillol, Bonnard, Vlaminck, Ma-
tisse; also temporary exhibitions of modern art.
Hours: Tuesday, 2–5; other days, 10–12 and 2–5.
Admission: Free.

Lucerne [*Luzern*]
• KUNSTMUSEUM, Robert Zündstrasse 1. Includes
Swiss, French, German and Belgian art of the 20 century;
also temporary exhibitions.
Hours: Closed Monday (except August and September);
open other days, 10–12 and 2–5.
Admission: 1.50 Swiss francs.

Lugano
• MUSEO DI BELLE ARTI, Villa Ciani, Parco
Civico. Includes 20 century works by artists of the Canton
of Ticino, as well as modern foreign art.
Hours: Closed Monday; open other days, 9–12 and 2–6.

Neuchâtel
• MUSEE DES BEAUX-ARTS, 2 rue des Beaux-Arts
(main entrance, quai Léopold Robert), Tel: (038) 5 17 40.
Includes Swiss and French art of the 19 and 20 centuries
with works by Courbet, Corot, Hodler and others; also
temporary exhibitions.
Hours: Daily, 10–12 and 2–5.
Admission: Free, except during special exhibitions.

St. Gallen [*St. Gall*]
• KUNSTMUSEUM, Museumstrasse 32, Tel: (071)
24 88 02. Houses the Sturzeneggersche Gemäldesammlung
(Sturzenegger Painting Collection) and collections belonging to the municipality and the Kunstverein St. Gal-
len, works by Courbet, Corot, Monet, Pissarro, Sisley as
well as other 19 and 20 century European artists and a

special collection devoted to the art of Eastern Switzerland; also temporary exhibitions including modern art.
Hours: Closed Monday; open other days, 10–12 and 2–5.
Admission: Varies according to exhibition.

Solothurn

• MUSEUM DER STADT SOLOTHURN, Werkhofstrasse 30. Houses the municipal art collection including 19 and 20 century painting by Swiss artists with works by Hodler, Amiet and others; yearly exhibition of works by living Swiss artists.
Hours: Closed Monday; open Sunday, 10–12 and 2–4; other days, 9–12 and 2–5.
Admission: Sunday morning and Wednesday afternoon, free; other times, 1 Swiss franc.

Thun

• KUNSTSAMMLUNG DER STADT THUN (Art Collection of the Town of Thun), Thunerhof, Hofstettenstrasse, Tel: (033) 2 44 44. Contains collection of Swiss art from *c.* 1920; also temporary exhibitions.
Hours: Open during exhibitions only: Monday, 10–12; other days, 10–12 and 2–5, also Wednesday and Friday evenings, 8–9:30.
Admission: 1 Swiss franc.

Winterthur

• KUNSTMUSEUM, Museumstrasse 52, Tel: (052) 2 10 57. Contains Swiss art of 19 and 20 centuries with emphasis on Hodler, Vallotton, Auberjonois and French and German painting and sculpture of 19 and 20 centuries including works by Monet, Renoir, van Gogh, Bonnard, Vuillard, Corinth, Maillol, Hofer, Kokoschka; also temporary exhibitions.
Hours: Monday, 2–5; other days, 10–12 and 2–5.
Admission: Wednesday, Saturday and Sunday afternoons, free; other times, 55 centimes.

• STIFTUNG OSKAR REINHART (Oskar Reinhart Foundation), Stadthausstrasse 6, Tel: (052) 2 97 61. Includes works by Swiss, German and Austrian artists of 19 and 20 centuries which once formed part of Dr. Oskar Reinhart's private collection; artists represented are, among others, Daumier, Courbet, Cézanne, Renoir, van Gogh, Toulouse-Lautrec, Picasso.

Hours: Monday, 2–5; other days, 10–12 and 2–5, also first Thursday evening of month, 8–10.

Admission: Adults: Wednesday and Sunday afternoons, 50 centimes; other times, 1.50 Swiss francs (whole-day tickets, 2 Swiss francs); children: 50 centimes.

Zürich

• KRONENHALLE, Rämistrasse 4, Tel: (051) 32 66 69. Café-restaurant which houses the large private collection of 19 and 20 century art of Gustav Zumsteg including works by Daumier, Redon, Signac, Cézanne, Matisse, La Fresnaye, Léger, Picasso, Klee, de Chirico, Miró, Tanguy, Giacometti and many others.

Hours: Daily, 10 a.m.–12 p.m.

Admission: Free.

• KUNSTGEWERBEMUSEUM (Museum of Arts and Crafts), Ausstellungstrasse 60, Tel: (051) 42 67 00. Collection of applied art, graphic art and industrial design not on permanent exhibition; organizes regular temporary exhibitions including modern art.

Hours: Saturday and Sunday, 10–12 and 2–5; Monday, 2–6; other days, 10–12 and 2–6, also Tuesday and Thursday evenings, 8–10.

Admission: Free.

• KUNSTHAUS, Heimplatz, Tel: (051) 32 17 22. Includes Swiss and foreign painting and sculpture from 19 century to the present with, among others, Daumier,

Monet, Cézanne, Renoir, van Gogh, Bonnard, Rouault, Matisse, Léger, Picasso, Beckmann, Kokoschka, Klee and a great number of works by Munch and Hodler; also temporary exhibitions.

Hours: Monday, 2–5; other days, 10–5, also Tuesday–Friday evenings, 8–10.

Admission: Sunday and Wednesday afternoons, free; other times, 2.50 Swiss francs.

Publications:

Werk, Swiss monthly for art, architecture, applied arts, Meisenstrasse 1, Winterthur.

Schweizer Kunst, Art Suisse, Arte Svizzera, publication of the Society of Swiss Painters, Sculptors and Architects, Habsburgstrasse 14, Bern.

Calder: Black Flower. Pushkin State Museum, Moscow

U.S.S.R.

Leningrad

• THE HERMITAGE, M. Dvortsovaya Naberezhnaya 9. "No group of French paintings outside the Parisian galleries can compare with the Leningrad and Moscow collections . . . ." Charles Sterling, *Great French Painting in the Hermitage,* Harry N. Abrams, Inc., New York, 1958. A few of the modern artists represented are Courbet, Corot, Cézanne, van Gogh, Vuillard, Derain, Matisse, Picasso.

Moscow

• PUSHKIN STATE MUSEUM OF FINE ARTS, Volkhonka 12. Includes, among many others, works by Courbet, Millet, Monet, Renoir, Degas, Cézanne, van Gogh, Gauguin, Denis, Henri Rousseau, Vuillard, Utrillo, Matisse, Picasso.

• TRETYAKOV STATE GALLERY, Laorushinsky per. 10. Includes 19 and 20 century works by Russian painters, sculptors and graphic artists.

John: Dylan Thomas. National Museum of Wales

WALES

Cardiff [*Glamorgan*]
• NATIONAL MUSEUM OF WALES, Cathays Park,
Tel: 26241.
Hours: Sunday, 2:30–5; other days, 10–5, April–September, Thursday, 10–8.
Admission: Sunday, 6 pence; other days, free.

Swansea [*Glamorgan*]
• GLYNN VIVIAN ART GALLERY, Alexandra Road,
Tel: 55006. Includes contemporary British painting,
sculpture and drawings.
Hours: Closed Sunday; open other days, 10–6.
Admission: Free.

YUGOSLAVIA

Belgrade [*Beograd*]
• Narodni Muzej (National Museum), Trg
Republike 1, Tel: 624 322.
Hours: Closed Monday; open Tuesday and Friday eve-
   nings, 5–9; other days, 9–1.
Admission: 20 dinars.

Dubrovnik
• Umjetnicka Galerija (Art Gallery), Put
Frana Supila 19, Tel: 20 61.

Ljubljana
• Moderna Galerija (Modern Gallery),
Presernova 15, Tel: 21 709. Collection of modern Slovenian art from impressionism to the present; also temporary
exhibitions including the "Mednarodna Grafiěna Razs-
tava" (International Biennial of Graphic Arts).
Hours: Sunday, 10–1; Wednesday and Friday, 2–6.

• Narodna Galerija (National Gallery), Prezi-
hova ulica 1, Tel: 21 765. Includes Slovenian art of the
19 and 20 centuries.
Hours: Sunday, Thursday and Saturday, 10–1.

Zagreb
• Gradska Galerija Savremene Umjetnosti
(City Gallery of Modern Art), Katarinski Trg. 2.

• Moderna Galerija (Modern Gallery), Braće
Kavurića 1. Modern Croatian art.